Table of CONTENTS

ESL BASICS

SENTENCES

WORD CHOICE

EDITING FOR GRAMMAR

PUNCTUATION

SELECTED ANSWERS TO EXERCISES

A Note to Instructors

Thank you for adopting *The Writer's Brief Handbook, Canadian Edition,* and its companion, *Exercise Book* for *The Writer's Brief Handbook*. This exercise book has been designed to help your students practise the many points made in *The Writer's Brief Handbook*. In general, for each rule in the *Handbook* one or more exercises are presented. Most exercises contain ten problems, and answers for the first five problems are included at the back of this book. A full set of answers is available in a separate publication, entitled the *Answer Key*. Thus, your students can work independently on numbers 1–5 and the remaining problems can be used for homework, quizzes, or as additional practice for students needing help in learning a particular rule or concept.

Format

Each exercise set is explicitly keyed to the rules presented in the *Handbook*; for example, "GRAM 1a" refers you to the chapter "GRAMmar Essentials," section 1a. In order to further help you locate material, a table of contents is also provided.

Most of the exercises are double-spaced in order to provide room on the page for students to answer the problem by editing the original—thereby using the same techniques they will need to apply to their own writing.

Instructors who have assigned *The Writer's Brief Handbook* as a textbook may duplicate any or all of these exercises and the answers in the *Answer Key* for distribution to students. The *Exercise Book* may also be purchased by students. In addition, the *Handbook* and the *Exercise Book* are available for purchase as a shrink-wrapped package at a special discount. Instructors interested in additional information on this package discount should call their Allyn & Bacon Canada representative.

PREFACE

Good writing demands a lot of hard work from the author: creative thinking, to find a message worth communicating; writing and revising, to express and refine that message; and editing, to polish that message into its most persuasive form for a particular audience. The number and variety of tasks faced by an author from start to finish can sometimes seem daunting, but writing, like most complex tasks, becomes much more manageable when it is approached as a series of smaller subtasks. *The Writer's Brief Handbook, Canadian Edition,* presents writing, revising, and editing as a series of "rules"—the subtasks to be mastered by every author who seeks to produce good work.

Moreover, writing—perhaps more than almost any other "academic" subject—requires active learning. Reading about how to write is just the beginning. You also need to write regularly and consciously apply the rules in *The Writer's Brief Handbook.* This exercise book is designed to help you actively develop your writing skills by providing intensive practise of the points made in the *Handbook.*

The chapters in the *Exercise Book* refer to those in the *Handbook*:

- Chapter 1, Composing (COMP)
- Chapter 2, Paragraphs (PARA)
- Chapter 3, Grammar Essentials (GRAM)
- Chapter 4, ESL Basics (ESL)
- Chapter 5, Sentences (SENT)
- Chapter 6, Word Choice (WORD)
- Chapter 7, Editing for Grammar (EDIT)
- Chapter 8, Punctuation (PUNCT)
- Chapter 9, Mechanics (MECH)
- Chapter 10, Essentials of Formatting (FORMAT))
- Chapter 11, The Library (LIB)
- Chapter 12, The Research Paper (RESCH)
- Chapter 13, MLA Style Documentation (MLA DOCU)
- Chapter 14, Other Systems of Documentation (OTHER DOCU)
- Selected Answers to Exercises

In general, for each rule in the *Handbook* one or more exercises are presented. Most exercises contain ten problems, and answers for the first five are included at the back of this book.

Using This Book

Before beginning an exercise, we suggest you read completely the section in the *Handbook* from which the exercise is drawn. All exercises are cross-referenced to *The Writer's Brief Handbook*; for example, "GRAM 1a" refers you to the chapter **GRAM**mar Essentials, section **1a**. If you have trouble with an exercise you can return to the cross-referenced section in the *Handbook*. But be sure to try the exercises first on your own! Once you complete an exercise, you can check your answers to problems 1–5 by referring to the answer section at the back of this book.

Possible Solutions

Many of the exercises present sentences with errors for you to correct. Often there is more than one correct solution. The answer section of this workbook generally only provides you with one possible solution. It is beyond the scope of this workbook to present multiple solutions and discuss the rationale for each. Thus, if your answer for an exercise differs from the one in the answer section and you believe your solution is correct—or you don't understand why the answer given in this book is correct—be sure to see your instructor. English is an impressively flexible language, and you may well have found another equally valid solution.

Typography

In the exercises, type that should be displayed in italics, such as the title of a book, is in *italics*. However, as you will most likely write your answers by hand, you won't have access to italic type. Use, therefore, the comparable editor's mark—underlining—to indicate italics. The answers provided in the book follow this pattern. For example:

Exercise: Whom is the author of *The Hitchhiker's Guide to the Galaxy*?

Correction: Who is the author of <u>The Hitchhiker's Guide to the Galaxy</u>?

Editing versus Rewriting

Your instructor will guide you as to how to use this book, but for many exercises you can make written corrections directly on the page, rather than rewrite the entire sentence to make the needed changes. This is, in fact, how editors mark up manuscripts; so it's not just a shortcut, but good professional technique. It also eliminates the possible introduction of new errors due to miscopying. The answer section, however, presents completely rewritten sentences.

Abbreviations

The following abbreviations are used in the exercises to refer to and label words, phrases, and clauses:

ADJ CLS = adjective (relative) clause
ADV CLS = adverb clause
COORD = coordinating conjunction
CORREL = correlative conjunction
DO = direct object
GER = gerund
INF = infinitive
IO = indirect object
NOUN CLS = noun clause
PA = predicate adjective
PN = predicate noun
PAST PART = past participle
PRES PART = present participle
SUB = subordinating conjunction
Vi = verb, intransitive
Vl = verb, linking
Vt = verb, transitive

Chapter 1

COMPOSING

COMP 5c, Proofreading

Proofread the writing excerpt that begins on the following page. Mark up the sample essay as you would your own work, making changes on the page. There are twenty items that need correction.

For example:

> When I travel I always, or at least usually, carry along with me at
>
> least teh following items; shave kit, extra socks, and an extra Fifty
>
> Dollars folded inside my shoe. These items has bailed me out of more
>
> tight situations then I care to mension.

Answer:

ndent 5 spaces

 When I travel I always, ~~or at least usually,~~ carry along with me at
 wdy

: least ~~teh~~ the following items; shave kit, extra socks, and an extra Fifty
^ *f*

 Dollars folded inside my shoe. These items has bailed me out of more
d *ve*

 tight situations then I care to mension.
a *t*

"The Perils Of Astroturf"

Andy Pellet

As a purist and a sports fan, I am suspicious of
changes in my favourite pasttimes, namely, baseball and
football. In the past too decades, there has been many
new developments--some good and some bad. But the most
disturbing change is the introduction of artificial turf
as a playing surface; because it makes the game's unnatu-
ral and causes injuries.

This fake grass first appeared on the sporting scene
in 1966, according to the *Houston Chronicle*. The grass in
the Houston Astrodome was dying, so in desparation it
replaced by artificial turf. This new surface, manufac-
tured by the Monsanto Company, was appropriately called
"AstroTurf". Since the time of its first appearance on
the sporting scene in 1966, the living grass in the sta-
diums and playing fields have been replaced with one form
of artificial turf or another, usually made of green ny-
lon fibers stiched over a cushioned polyester mat, Astro-
Turf is still the most common.
What's so great about artificial turf? If real grass was
good enough for the sports heros of yesteryear, why
shouldn't it be good enough for today's? The proponents
of artificial turf have two basic arguments.

The first arguement used a familiar line of reason-
ing: artificial turf saved money. The field needs less….

2

Chapter 2

PARAGRAPHS

PARA 1, Unity

Examine each of the following sample paragraphs for unity. First underline the topic sentence of each paragraph. Then cross out any words, phrases, or clauses in the paragraph that do not develop the topic sentence.

For example:

> The most important day I remember in all my life is the one on which my teacher, Anne Mansfield Sullivan, came to me. I am filled with wonder when I consider the immeasurable contrast between the two lives that it connects. It was the third of March, 1887, three months before I was seven years old. The spring had been seasonable and pleasant.

Answer:

> <u>The most important day I remember in all my life is the one on which my teacher, Anne Mansfield Sullivan, came to me.</u> I am filled with wonder when I consider the immeasurable contrast between the two lives that it connects. It was the third of March, 1887, three months before I was seven years old. ~~The spring had been seasonable and pleasant.~~

—modified from Helen Keller, *The Story of My Life*

1. Mental models, our conceptual models of the ways objects work, events take place, or people behave, result from our tendency to form explanations of things. These models are essential in helping us understand our experiences, predict the outcomes of our actions, and handle unexpected occurrences. Unexpected occurrences can happen at any time. We base our models on whatever knowledge we have, real or imaginary, naive or sophisticated.

    —modified from Donald Norman, *The Psychology of Everyday Things*

2. The market is as much a part of your company as you are. After all, it represents one-half of the ledger. To grow, your business must earn the permission of the marketplace. No concept is more important for the start-up entrepreneur. Guarantees are an essen-

tial component. Customers must give your business permission to sell to them. They do this (at least as repeat customers) only after a thorough assessment of you, your product or service, and your operation. This is why Detroit is having trouble selling cars even though they're better built than they were. Fortunately this hasn't been a problem in the aerospace industry. These cars have to overcome years of bad notices. It will take time to accomplish this. In fact, it may take until there's a complete turnover in the market— until those of us who now think Japanese or German no longer drive.

—modified from Paul Hawken, *Growing a Business*

3. A classical understanding sees the world primarily as underlying form itself. A romantic understanding sees it primarily in terms of immediate appearance. If you were to show an engine or a mechanical drawing or an electronic schematic to a romantic it is unlikely he would see much in it. It has no appeal because the reality he sees is its surface. Dull, complex lists of names, lines and numbers. Nothing interesting. Classification systems may say more about their creators than about the objects being classified. But if you were to show the same blueprint or schematic or give the same description to a classical person, he might look at it and then become fascinated by it because he sees that within the lines and shapes and symbols is a tremendous richness of underlying form.

—modified from Robert Pirsig, *Zen and the Art of Motorcycle Maintenance*

4. At a certain season of our life we are accustomed to consider every spot as the possible site of a house. I have thus surveyed the country on every side within a dozen miles of where I live. In imagination I have bought all the farms in succession, for all were to be bought, and I knew their price. I enjoy walking and find it a healthful relaxation. I walked over each farmer's premises, tasted his wild apples, discoursed on husbandry with him, and took his farm at his price.

—modified from Henry David Thoreau, *Walden*

5. As the rules of chess define the game of chess, linguistic rules define the game of language, which would not exist without them. They are not strict mechanism of cause and effect—one thing simply making another thing happen—but a system essentially open and incomplete, so that it is always capable of novelty. Rules of etiquette close off a system, keeping it uniform and predictable unless the rules are changed. Who is allowed to change these rules? When can such changes be made? Rules of language are indirect and can be used again and again on the same finite set of letters and words, making possible an open universe of new sentences on the closed universe of the dictionary. Dictionaries you will have noticed are printed, not spoken.

   —modified from Jeremy Campbell, *Grammatical Man*

6. Macintosh Way marketing is the *marketing of technology*—finding the right people and getting the right information into their hands. The cost of this approach is not important. Frequently businesses take other strategies which yield different results. The foundation of this approach is that customers have a deep understanding of what they want, how things should work, and what they are willing to tolerate. They are attracted, not intimidated, by innovation and technology. They actually use and like great products.

   —modified from Guy Kawasaki, *The Macintosh Way*

7. The relative strengths of the leading nations in world affairs never remain constant, principally because of the uneven rate of growth among different societies and of the technological and organizational breakthroughs which bring a greater advantage to one society than to another. If, however, too large a proportion of the state's wealth is diverted from wealth creation and allocated instead to military purposes, then that is likely to lead to a weakening of national power over the longer term. Population growth has not shown a demonstrable effect in this pattern of controlled growth.

   —modified from Paul Kennedy, *The Rise and Fall of the Great Powers*

8. The stock market crash of 1929 brought to light substantial inadequacies in financial reporting. Investigations of bankrupt companies showed numerous arithmetic errors and cases of undetected

fraud. The status of healthy companies is largely unknown. The investigations also disclosed the common use of a widely varying set of accounting practices. The 1920s were arguably a time of greater freedom. A principal outcome of these investigations was that the [government] required that publicly held companies must annually issue a report to shareholders. The reports are generally distributed via Second or Third Class delivery. The report must contain financial statements prepared by the firm's management and audited by an accountant.

—modified from Steven Winkler, *The Complete Guide to Finance & Accounting for Nonfinance Managers*

9. Scarcely thirty kilometres divide Zanzibar from the African mainland, and on a clear day you can plainly see the island from the coast. A motor launch accomplished the journey across the straits in an hour or two and makes a sound frequently reported as terrifying by the local inhabitants. By air the trip is a matter of ten or fifteen minutes. Yet there is an astonishing difference between the island and the mainland shore. In Zanzibar everything is soft and beguiling. The currents in this region are swift. Zanzibar is as relaxing as a Turkish bath.

—modified from Alan Moorehead, *The White Nile*

10. Throughout the inhabited world, in all times and under every circumstance, the myths of man have flourished; and they have been the living inspiration of whatever else may have appeared out of the activities of the human body and mind. It is not appropriate to consider our physical beings as mere biology. It would not be too much to say that myth is the secret opening through which inexhaustible energies of the cosmos pour into human cultural manifestation. Business is not included in this analysis. Religions, philosophies, arts, the social forms of primitive and historic man, prime discoveries in science and technology, the very dreams that blister sleep, boil up from the basic, magic ring of myth. Anthropologists sometimes are the ones to carry out this investigative work.

—modified from Joseph Campbell, *The Hero with a Thousand Faces*

PARA 2b, Development Strategies 1

There are many methods of developing and organizing information both on the scale of the paragraph and the essay as a whole. For example:

Narration: telling a story, most often relating events in chronological order.

Description: describing scenes, most often ordering the items spatially, as a movie camera might capture a scene.

Examples and illustration: citing examples.

Facts, statistics, reasons: using factual information, including numerical summaries.

Definition: providing an extended definition.

Process analysis: explaining a procedure, usually in a step-by-step description.

Comparison and contrast: comparing two things (demonstrating their similarities) and/or contrasting things (demonstrating their dissimilarities).

Analogy: comparing a complex or unfamiliar subject to another topic typically more widely known and understood.

Classification: grouping topics into larger classes on the basis of one or more criterion that demonstrate shared similarities.

Cause and effect: explaining the causal link between two or more subjects.

Mixed strategies: employing more than one of the preceding strategies.

Many of the paragraphs in the preceeding exercise use mixed strategies. Referring back to the sample paragraphs on pages 3–6, list for each the development strategy(ies) you think the author uses.

For example: Helen Keller, *The Story of My Life*:

Answer: narration
_____

1. Donald Norman, *The Psychology of Everyday Things*:
_____

2. Paul Hawken, *Growing a Business*:
_____

3. Robert Pirsig, *Zen and the Art of Motorcycle Maintenance*:
_____

4. Henry David Thoreau, *Walden*:
_____

5. Jeremy Campbell, *Grammatical Man:*

   _____

6. Guy Kawasaki, *The Macintosh Way:*

   _____

7. Paul Kennedy, *The Rise and Fall of the Great Powers:*

   _____

8. Steven Winkler, *The Complete Guide to Finance & Accounting for Nonfinance Managers:*

   _____

9. Alan Moorehead, *The White Nile:*

   _____

10. Joseph Campbell, *The Hero with a Thousand Faces:*

    _____

PARA 2b, Development Strategies 2

For each writing assignment listed here, provide one or more development strategies that you could successfully employ to write on that topic. (If necessary, refer back to the list of development strategies on page 7.)

For example: Explain the concept of separation of power within Canadian government.

Answer: *definition; illustration*

1. Explain how college basketball has changed in the last decade.

2. Discuss the operations of United Nations' peacekeeping forces.

3. Explain the slower-than-expected adoption of recycling.

4. Describe the impact of the Canadian deficit on our economy.

5. Describe the most important day in your life.

6. Describe the differences between attending college as an eighteen-year-old compared to returning to school as an adult.

7. Explain what a family is.

8. What is privacy in the electronic age?

9. Discuss homelessness in Canada.

10. Discuss changes in automobile manufacturing.

PARA 3, Coherence 1

Writers use four principal tools to make their writing coherent: organization, transitions, repetition of key words and phrases, and parallel structures.

After reading the following passage complete the exercises that follow it.

When I was fourteen, my father's last reassignment took my whole family to Kenya for nearly two years. We arrived right after New Year's Day. Our new home, "the station," was fifty kilometres out into the bush, and every other Saturday my parents, my sister, and I made the long drive into town. The road was rough, a rutted trail in some places, and our Land Rover ground along at never more than fifty kilometres an hour, all of us sweltering in this mechanical beast. It was an adventure the first few trips, but became a misery after that. On the Saturday just before our first Easter, we were again making the drive, everyone slapping about inside like raggedy dolls, and no one speaking because it was too noisy and because our moods were too close to foul. Suddenly my father yelled "Look," and pointed off to the left side.

He threw in the clutch and we coasted. Everyone in the truck turned to watch. A herd of bok had appeared on the hillside along the road and they were running full tilt. Before I could even finish asking myself why, the reason appeared: a cheetah, running at top speed. Furiously fast but so smooth it seemed to be riding on an invisible rail, the cat cut across the hill, arcing for a trailing bok. And even as I leaned forward to see better, it was already over: down went the cheetah and bok, the cheetah with his jaws wrapped around his prey's throat. Neither animal seemed to struggle. They lay suddenly still together, in a strange embrace. I could hear nothing but the sound of our engine. The two animals did not move, their silent dance of dust and speed and sere grass was done.

"Won't see much of that round here in a few years," said my father, letting the clutch back out too quickly, lurching the Rover. My head bounced hard on the door pillar.

"Ow," I yelled. I pressed my fingers to my right temple, and almost immediately a welt began to rise against my fingertips. The lump felt hot and wet. Was it blood or sweat? Overcoming this distraction, I called out to my father, "Why will we see cheetahs in a few years? I mean," I stammered, "why won't we?"

"Poaching," said my father without emotion, driving on. I strained in my seat, looking back through the mud-splattered windows, holding my head. The two animals were now out of sight, obscured by the grass. I continued to look back for another several minutes. My family rode on without speaking, the Rover grinding steadily through the landscape.

—Christopher Bray, "Voyages from Home"

1. How is the sample passage organized? (Chronologically? Spatially? Logically?) Explain your choice.

2. Underline the transitional words and phrases in the story. How do they relate to the type of organization used by the author?

PARA 3, Coherence 2

Writers use four principal tools to make their writing coherent: organization, transitions, repetition of key words and phrases, and parallel structures.

After reading the following passage complete the exercises that follow it.

When I worked on a farm, we managed herds. We managed rangeland. Friends managed feedlots. So I am amused but dismayed when someone talks about managing people. You don't ever manage people—you *work with* them. For your business to succeed, you must take exceedingly good care of your people. This is not a chore or a responsibility, it is the most rewarding aspect of being in business, yet it is the area in which most businesses, large and small, fail.

If people are honest about it, you will find that the majority of them are not satisfied with their jobs, their work, or their relationship with "management." One of the strongest reasons so many people want to go into business for themselves is not the allure of business, but a desire to get away from their current stifling jobs. It is well within your power as a businessperson to create an atmosphere that is not stifling.

—Paul Hawken, *Growing a Business*

1. How is the sample passage organized? (Chronologically? Spatially? Logically?) Explain your choice.

2. Underline the words or phrases repeated by the author. What is the effect of this repetition?

PARA 3, Coherence 3

Writers use four principal tools to make their writing coherent: organization, transitions, repetition of key words and phrases, and parallel structures.

After reading the following passage complete the exercises that follow it.

I can see by my watch, without taking my hand from the left grip of the cycle, that it is eight-thirty in the morning. The wind, even at sixty miles a hour, is warm and humid. When it's this hot and muggy at eight-thirty, I'm wondering what it's going to be like in the afternoon.

In the wind are pungent odours from the marshes by the road. We are in an area of the Central Plains filled with thousands of duck hunting sloughs, heading northwest. This highway is an old concrete two-laner that hasn't had much traffic since a four-laner went in parallel to it several years ago. When we pass a marsh the air suddenly becomes cooler. Then, when we are past, it suddenly warms up again.

—modified from Robert Pirsig, *Zen and the Art of Motorcycle Maintenance*

1. How is the sample passage organized? (Chronologically? Spatially? Logically?) Explain your choice.

2. Underline the parallel structures. What is the effect of these structures?

Chapter 3

GRAMMAR ESSENTIALS

GRAM 1a, Verbs

For each of the sentences, underline the verb and related item and label them as follows:

- If the verb is linking, underline both the verb and the predicate adjective(s) or predicate noun(s) (Vl, PA, PN).
- If the verb is transitive, underline both the verb and the indirect or direct object(s) (Vt, IO, DO).
- If the verb is intransitive, underline only the verb (Vi).

For example: Ollie <u>cut</u> <u>the boards</u>.
               Vt   DO

1. Tina swims in the pool on Tuesdays.

2. John gave Fred a birthday present.

3. The weather seems fine today.

4. Shelby bought her textbooks at the campus bookstore.

5. Jorge is a tenor.

6. Bread was delivered to the flood victims by the army.

7. The army gave the flood victims bread.

8. Biotechnology has required a very substantial investment.

9. Nanna wrote me a long letter.

10. Bahna sings for her church choir.

GRAM 1b, Nouns

Complete the following table. Consult a dictionary if necessary.
For example:

SINGULAR	PLURAL	SINGULAR POSSESSIVE	PLURAL POSSESSIVE
pen	pens	pen's	pens'
1. dish			
2. hero			
3. book			
4. wife			
5. man			
6. boss			
7. fish			
8. roof			
9. sky			
10. criterion			

GRAM 1c, Pronouns

Underline the pronouns in the following sentences.
For example: Doris gave <u>it</u> to <u>me</u>, but <u>I</u> told <u>her</u> <u>it</u> wasn't <u>mine</u>.

1. I gave Donald a call.

2. I spoke to him yesterday.

3. He usually has to call me back.

4. Raspberries are ready at their farm.

5. Which farm, McGuire's?

6. Yes, everybody loves their fresh fruit.

7. I often go the library by myself.

8. Our teacher reminded us to begin our research papers early.

9. Josie's paper on recycling was more interesting than mine.

10. Because the Vancouver Art Gallery was closed, we went to the Art Gallery of Greater Victoria.

GRAM 1d, Adjectives

Choose the correct adjectival form (positive, comparative, or superlative) and underline your selection in each sentence that follows.
For example: Is the CN Tower still the world's (tall, taller, tallest)?

1. If presented with Häagen-Daz and Ben & Jerry's, could you say which is (creamy, creamier, creamiest)?

2. The *Edmonton Journal* declined to name the (good, better, best) candidate amongst the five potential nominees.

3. Jack is (old, older, oldest) than his brother John.

4. Jack is the (old, older, oldest) of the four children.

5. Before starting the 108 riders, the judge called, "May the (good, better, best) cyclist win!"

6. I've eaten a lot of good strawberry shortcakes, but I still think my mom's is (good, better, best).

7. Khalil and Sollie can never agree which is (fun, more fun, the most fun)—skiing or surfing.

8. The meteorologist said that yesterday may have been hot, but today would be (hot, hotter, hottest).

9. He also said that last Thursday was the (hot, hotter, hottest) day this summer.

10. Cora told me that the Lake Superior was (big, bigger, biggest) than Lake Huron and Lake Erie.

GRAM 1e, Adverbs

Underline the adverbs in the following sentences.

For example: Things cook <u>more</u> <u>slowly</u> in Lake Louise than Brandon because of the altitude.

1. John runs fast.

2. Of all the sopranos, Lena sang the most beautifully.

3. The commute home always seemed longer than the one to the office.

4. After the thunderstorm, steam rose eerily from the still warm pavement.

5. Jackson was tired but worked hard to finish the assigned reading before going to bed.

6. For a city so small, Charlottetown is surprisingly beautiful.

7. High-speed rail may change how frequently we fly to Montreal.

8. Ellen was very happy to discover that the most important book in her bibliography had not been checked out of the library.

9. The children of immigrants rarely know much about their parents' homeland.

10. The vase of freshly cut peonies gave the room a wonderful smell.

GRAM 1f, Prepositions

In the folllowing sentences, enclose the complete prepositional phrases in parentheses and underline the prepositions.

For example: I walked (<u>to</u> the grocery, the fruit stand, and the bank).

1. On the move since dawn, the hikers had advanced thirty kilometres by lunchtime.

2. Sara finished three of the four essay questions quickly.

3. Chu's nieces and nephews danced around the room.

4. Bill saw his token roll into the street and disappear down a storm drain.

5. Forty-seven storeys above the street, the falcons built their nest on one of the building's gargoyles.

6. After delivering the newspapers, Susan's hands were black with ink.

7. The river wound its way into town from the east.

8. In the excitement, I couldn't remember who came after me in the lineup.

9. The 1989 Memorial Cup final is still one of Harlin's favourites.

10. Carol's hook shot bounced off the rim just after the buzzer sounded.

GRAM 1g, Conjunctions

In the following sentences, enclose the conjunction-containing clauses in parentheses. Then underline the conjunctions and label them as coordinating (COORD), subordinating (SUB), or correlative (CORREL).

For example: (If I had more money), I would replace my old car. (SUB)

1. I went to the store before Sushmito arrived.

2. It rained all night, so the tournament was postponed.

3. I like to fish even though I don't catch anything most days.

4. Although exercise is important, there are days when I prefer to just lounge around on the beach.

5. Professor Stanley asked us not only to compare and contrast Laurence and Mitchell, but also to use one or more of their works to support our points.

6. As the sun rose over Great Slave Lake, the water became faceted with dancing white light.

7. Outside the cabin it was cold and windy, but inside it was warm and quiet.

8. My grandfather used to say, "It's time to either cut bait or fish."

9. Rich and Gary, when they saw the long line for tickets, decided to go home and watch the game on television.

10. She disliked the medicine more than I.

GRAM 2a, Subjects

For each sentence that follows, underline the complete subject in the main clause.

For example: <u>Why anybody would live anyplace other than Nova Scotia</u> was a mystery to Annie.

1. My dog sleeps so much that my roommate thinks she's a stuffed animal.

2. Ly's enthusiasm for our annual reunion is infectious.

3. Joan's track and swimming talents earned her a scholarship.

4. Calculus 201 and Chemistry 137 have kept me extremely busy this semester.

5. The university has five libraries.

6. Riding the noisy subway to school ensures that I am completely awake by the time I get off.

7. Branagh's remakes of *Henry V* and *Much Ado* have brought Shakespeare to new audiences.

8. There are many ways to define success.

9. Rain, rain, and more rain brought the river and its many tributaries to record levels.

10. The debate over national unity has raised many difficult questions.

GRAM 2b, Predicates

Underline the complete predicate in each of the following sentences.
For example: I <u>work in Enrico's Deli from 8 to 11 weeknights.</u>

1. Smoking is expensive and addictive.

2. Jacques believed that his studies were a worthwhile investment.

3. Melissa's research paper explored the differences between personal debt and the federal debt.

4. Gwen is the oldest of five children.

5. Bill and Ted cooked dinner together most nights.

6. Cronston Avenue ends just beyond Main Street.

7. Lions sleep during much of the day.

8. Rajiv was happy he had backed up his hard disk when it crashed only a day later.

9. Nevin was disappointed to find that all of the concert tickets had been sold.

10. Though Eliza lived on the sixth floor, she created a garden of tomatoes, lettuce, onions, and herbs by planting in window boxes.

GRAM 3b, Verbals

In the following sentences, underline the verbals and verbal phrases. Then identify their type as gerund (GER), infinitive (INF), past participle (PAST PART), or present participle (PRES PART).

For example: <u>Comparing Maurice Richard and Wayne Gretzky as hockey players</u> would be interesting. (PRES PART)

1. I love running because it requires so little equipment.

2. Pacing yourself during an exam is crucial.

3. The drummer playing the timbales is my cousin.

4. The rebel army, faced with many hardships, managed to defeat the better trained and equipped enemy.

5. To conduct good science requires first, good training; second, good insight; and third, great effort.

6. Shooting the jumper in basketball is a lot easier when you plant both feet firmly before leaping.

7. The bird singing in the top of that maple is a Golden Finch.

8. My grandmother always urged me to believe in myself.

9. Feeling the wind come up suddenly, Maggie suspected a thunderstorm was approaching.

10. Stretching out before running is increasingly important as you age, especially to prevent injuries.

GRAM 4, Clauses

Underline and label the adjective (relative) clauses (ADJ CLS), adverb clauses (ADV CLS), and noun clauses (NOUN CLS) in the following sentences.

For example: The fish <u>that live in our lake</u> have been reduced in numbers recently by an increase in pollution. (ADJ CLS)

1. When I saw Roger, who was just returning from a trip, he told me he would be playing softball with us this Saturday.

2. Ceilia painted her house purple because it was her favourite colour.

3. If you hit or tip a ball foul and you already have two strikes, the count remains unchanged.

4. He hoped his contribution to the charity would benefit whoever was most in need.

5. After losing three games straight, the team was overjoyed when it beat the undefeated first place team.

6. At the party on the night before he left for college, everyone wished him well.

7. My motorcycle was magnificent when it ran and a great frustration the rest of the time.

8. Milo's family came over after they finished their dinner.

9. He knew a good deal when he saw it.

10. Our school's library, which was built in 1883, is a fine example of H. H. Richardson's work.

GRAM 5, Types of Sentences

Classify each of the following sentences by type: simple, compound, complex, or compound-complex.

For example: I reeled the fish in, and Bill netted it. (compound)

1. Though ink may look black, it also contains red pigment.

2. Fred likes to read in bed.

3. Blue Jays and Cardinals are examples of birds that remain in Southern Ontario over the winter.

4. After scooping ice cream all summer, my right arm was so strong that I could beat my older brother in arm wrestling, and my left arm looked so withered to me that it seemed almost useless, like the forelegs of *Tyrannosaurus rex*.

5. Though it may sound odd, I swim in the winter and ski in the summer.

6. I read the book and wrote my analysis all in one day.

7. Lynn went from meeting to meeting until three o'clock, and then she caught a cab to the airport for her four o'clock flight.

8. I saved my money until I had enough to buy a laptop computer.

9. I repainted our room before my roommate returned from spring break, and all he could say when he saw it was that I must be colourblind.

10. Though there is much strife in the world, I maintain my optimism because I do not believe in types of people, only individuals.

Chapter 4

ESL BASICS

ESL 1a, Modal Auxiliaries
Correct the use of modal auxiliaries in the following sentences.
For example: Nick will not to swim in the lake with us.
Correction: Nick will not swim in the lake with us.

1. In one hour I be done.

2. You will to see me there tonight.

3. I should can finish this novel before class.

4. We cannot to come to the party.

5. When I was growing up, my family will usually take a trip in
   the summer.

6. Elly can is knowing how to operate the slide projector.

7. In ten minutes the eggs be ready.

8. Bernard can sings very well.

9. I can have to leave early.

10. He must cleaning up before he can go.

ESL 1b, Perfect Tenses

Correct the use of perfect tenses in the following sentences.

For example: She have found a nice new apartment.

Correction: She has found a nice new apartment.

1. They have travel too much this year to want to go on another trip soon.

2. We has expecting you yesterday.

3. Bill goes to the movies frequently; he will have saw that one already.

4. Chloë had sang in the choir for three years before she was chosen to be its director.

5. Suzanne have brung me flowers every year on my birthday.

6. The newspapers has watched the politician closely.

7. As of next spring, our organization will had support the children's hospital for twenty-five years.

8. I have drove on this road before.

9. They has gave Paulus an award two years in a row now.

10. She have raised a child even while enrolled in school.

ESL 1c, Progressive Tenses

Correct the use of progressive tenses in the following sentences.

For example: Lola been coming here every day.

Correction: Lola has been coming here every day.

1. John seeing René for the first time.

2. Sheila are giving her friends dancing lessons.

3. The ozone layer been thinning because of the release of CFCs.

4. Joanne is being happy today.

5. Sanga had be thinking calculus was easy until he took the midterm exam.

6. Jason is gone to the play tomorrow night.

7. They will working this afternoon on the scenery.

8. By the time Mr. Tottle retires next year, he will been teaching at NBHS for thirty-eight years.

9. They be discussing her newest record album.

10. Mary been cooking her favourite dinner all afternoon.

ESL 1d, Passive Voice 1

Correct the use of the passive voice in the following sentences.
For example: The siren was heared by everyone on the street.
Correction: The siren was heard by everyone on the street.

1. The NHL championship was winned by Montreal this year.

2. Africa is visit by many Canadians.

3. We were sitted by the hostess.

4. Many books is now published only in paperback.

5. Every student are expected to do well in his or her studies.

6. Many issues is discuss by the prime minister's cabinet.

7. John were racked by the flu.

8. The national anthem was singed by Anne Murray.

9. My pants were burnt when I ironed with the temperature too high.

10. The night course were added because many people couldn't attend during the day.

ESL 1d, Passive Voice 2

Rewrite the following passive voice sentences in the active voice.
For example: The siren was heard by everyone on the street.
Correction: Everyone on the street heard the siren.

1. My backpack was lost yesterday by Tom.

2. The memorial to Canada's armed forces is seen by many commuters every day.

3. *Carmen* was written by Bizet.

4. Reading is enjoyed by many people.

5. Money was scrupulously saved by my parents.

6. A good time was had by all.

7. Affordable housing was spoken about by the City Council at every meeting.

8. The satellite was boosted into geostationary orbit by the space shuttle.

9. My daughter was thrilled by her graduation gift.

10. York was attacked by Mackenzie's rebels during the Rebellion of 1837.

ESL 1e, Two-Word Verbs

Correct the two-word verbs in the following sentences.
For example: Phil came a helpful article across.
Correction: Phil came across a helpful article.

1. Where's the newspaper? Oh, John threw away it?

2. The teacher called the student on.

3. Because of the extensive fire damage, the Fire Marshall ordered the building's owners to tear down it.

4. Simone heard her best friend from.

5. Why doesn't he pick someone on his own size?

6. The aspirin helped me get the cold over.

7. When you are in Moose Jaw, don't forget to look up me.

8. Look my cat after while I am away.

9. The TV is too loud; please turn down it.

10. My dad learned that smoking was unhealthy, so he gave up it.

ESL 1f, Verb Phrases

Correct the verb phrases in the following sentences.

For example: His father cautioned him using the crosswalk always.

Correction: His father cautioned him to use the crosswalk always.

1. They agreed come over here before the game.

2. Josef urged myself to see the film.

3. The boss permitted to take time off when my sister was married.

4. I imagine to fly is wonderful.

5. When I finish to eat, I'll read to you.

6. Please think about to save money for college.

7. Fred is beginning sounding good on the piano.

8. Sam manages living well on a modest income.

9. Otto's parents invited me come with them to the show.

10. My best friend suggested to see the school's career counsellors before going to the interview.

ESL 2a–c, Count and Noncount Nouns

Correct the use of count and noncount nouns in the following sentences.

For example: John bought two beefs at the butcher.
Correction: John bought two kilograms of beef at the butcher.

1. Gordon knows many local history.

2. How many breads did Orlo ask us to pick up?

3. Howard used two hundred pails of sands to build his huge sand castle.

4. Ryan said much machines are built there.

5. Don't put too many salt in the soup!

6. We received many, many snows here last winter.

7. My car used only 30 litres of gasolines for the 480-kilometre trip.

8. An information can be stored in a computer.

9. Canada mixes much cultures.

10. My grandfather and I cooked 8 kilogram of tomato.

ESL 2d, Definite Article

Correct the use of the definite article in the following sentences.

For example: I moved to the Regina when I was seven years old.
Correction: I moved to Regina when I was seven years old.

1. [To the waiter:] May I have the ketchup please?

   [Later, when it's already on the table:] Please pass some ketchup.

2. Mount Logan is highest peak in Canada.

3. I saw professor who won Nobel Prize last year.

4. The hockey is very popular here.

5. I saw the Bob walking down the hall just a minute ago.

6. I arrive at the work by 8 a.m. every day.

7. After graduating, Francine was hired by the Mohawk College.

8. Dora did not sing loudly, but her voice was best in the chorus.

9. I read last week that the calcium is important in your diet.

10. The New Brunswick's motto is "Hope was Restored."

ESL 3a, Cumulative Adjectives

Correct the word order of the adjectives in the following items.
For example: Réal lives in a brown big house.
Correction: Réal lives in a big brown house.

1. a pearl white long necklace

2. my new first bicycle

3. square five small buildings

4. a brick ancient fireplace

5. triangular large seven windows

6. a nineteenth-century elegant waltz

7. a wooden white fence

8. the German most knowledgeable jurist

9. some small older cabs

10. the hottest summer five days

ESL 3b, Present and Past Participles

Correct the following sentences by changing past and present participles as necessary.

For example: The NBA finals are always excited.

Correction: The NBA finals are always exciting.

1. Lola found the novel's ending surprised.

2. The winter winds here are very dried.

3. Sofia found organic chemistry fascinated.

4. Jackie's remarks annoying me.

5. The kitchen scene in *Jurassic Park* was frightened.

6. Many visitors find the highways around Toronto confused.

7. The ocean water refreshing me.

8. Jean saw depressed similarities in the history of the 1930s and the 1990s.

9. I found the actor's performance engaged.

10. Our hike into a strong wind all day left us exhausting.

ESL 3c, Adverb Placement

Correct the placement of adverbs in the following sentences.

For example: The food there always is good.

Correction: The food there is always good.

1. "The Last Post" is played traditionally on Remembrance Day.

2. There seems never to be enough time.

3. My older sister always is helpful.

4. I drove enough fast to get to work on time.

5. Louis went typically to the museum with his father.

6. Peter gave happily his present to his mother.

7. After the rainshower my clothes were enough wet to be wrung.

8. My dentist fails never to remind me to floss as well as brush.

9. John mailed early his package.

10. When she drove, she was focused extremely.

ESL 4a–c, Prepositions 1

Correct the use of prepositions in the following sentences.
For example: I prefer to travel in train rather than in plane.
Correction: I prefer to travel by train rather than by plane.

1. I went the movies nearly every week.

2. Francesca reads on the newspaper to improve her English.

3. When we first moved at Toronto, I missed Hong Kong very much.

4. Sari shops the grocery store everyday.

5. After his scholarship in Sardinia, Nova Scotia looked at very green.

6. Doug told me he works on his uncle's store.

7. Though I had read Shakespeare in translation before coming to Canada, I am finding it entirely new for English.

8. The 107 bus stops at here at quarter past and quarter of the hour.

9. Greg finished his story by time for class.

10. I would like to go the museum this Friday.

ESL 4d–f, Prepositions 2

Correct the use of prepositions in the following sentences.
For example: We called off our picnic because rain.
Correction: We called off our picnic because of rain.

1. Frederico was aware on the problem.

2. My brother's new glasses are for to read.

3. I walked as far Main Street before discovering that I had left my wallet at home.

4. How much is that equal of in dollars?

5. I like to paint as to well draw.

6. Due fog, the airport was closed.

7. "Come along me," called Gisela to Dave.

8. John was very proud for his diploma.

9. Addition to this book, you'll need that one.

10. Paul said, "After to exercise, stretch out and then shower."

ESL 5a–c, Subjects and Linking Verbs

Correct the following sentences by ensuring that each clause has one subject and that linking verbs are present when needed.
For example: My house, which was built in 1922, it has many architectural details not found in newer houses.
Correction: My house, which was built in 1922, has many architectural details not found in newer houses.

1. My school has three libraries. Will begin construction of a fourth soon.

2. Dirk's whole family very amusing.

3. The baseball league, it begins its season next week.

4. This reading assignment very long.

5. The cicadas in the trees in my neighbourhood they sing all day.

6. If clichés not true, why are they so often repeated?

7. My Great Uncle Tom, who loved to invent things, he was always fun to visit.

8. Dan's notebook, containing all his laboratory notes, it has been missing since yesterday.

9. My dinner, left too long in the oven, it became a black brick unrecognizable as food.

10. Our team won both games last week. Won last weekend, too.

ESL 5d, Expletives

Correct the use of expletives and verb agreement in the following sentences.

For example: Is a beautiful day today.
Correction: It is a beautiful day today.

1. There is three highways into downtown Montreal.

2. Here is my top choices for the position.

3. Here are the best recipe I have for turkey stuffing.

4. Is unlikely to rain when the sky is so clear.

5. There have many golf courses in Norfolk County.

6. Though the park is crowded, is still fun to be here.

7. She said there was two puppies for sale.

8. There is three variety stores on my block.

9. There are much speculation about why the dinosaurs disappeared.

10. Is true he won't run for another term as mayor?

ESL 6a, Questions with Who, Whom, and What

Correct the word order and helping verbs in the following questions containing *who*, *whom*, and *what*.

For example: What birds to migrate cause?

Correction: What causes birds to migrate?

1. Who are coming to dinner?

2. What highway gridlock create?

3. Whom the prime minister nominated?

4. Who today's mail brings in?

5. What the committee do?

6. Who is believing that explanation?

7. To who they sent the package?

8. What tides and currents in the ocean create?

9. Who take the bus to school?

10. What a good relationship does make for?

ESL 6b, Direct versus Indirect Questions

For each sentence, find the indirect question and rewrite it as a direct question.

For example: I don't know what time she's planning to arrive.

Answer: What time is she planning to arrive?

1. The proposal is unclear about how they will finance the new day-care centre.

2. He thought he knew which astronomer first identified and named M31.

3. My grandmother explained why my family came to this country in 1848.

4. She saw where the smoke was coming from.

5. Gena wonders how the Canadian Parliament differs from the British Parliament.

6. I wasn't sure when my uncle moved from Saint John to St. John's.

7. The engineers investigated how gravity affected the growth of crystals.

8. Robert didn't know when we could visit the Dow Planetarium in Montreal.

9. I would like to know what makes a good bus driver.

10. Pito asked me what I would give her for her birthday.

ESL 6b, Verbs and Word Order in Indirect Questions

Correct the following indirect questions by using proper word order and verbs.

For example: The lead story traced how has drug use changed in the last decade.

Correction: The lead story traced how drug use has changed in the last decade.

1. He asked me are you coming or not.

2. Rupert wasn't sure when did the Battle of Hastings occur.

3. I tried to see where did the rocket go.

4. The committee researched why has the cost of education outpaced inflation in the last ten years.

5. Everice asked do you enjoy playing racquetball.

6. The reporter asked when will we see the mayor's new budget.

7. I don't understand how does this lock work.

8. My nephew wondered did I want to go to the park with him.

9. I am not sure will you like pistachio ice cream.

10. I asked myself how can he be so late?

ESL 6c, Direct Quotations versus Reported Speech

For the following sentences, rewrite the direct quotations as reported speech and the reported speech as direct quotation.

Reported:　He said he'd been looking forward to meeting my family for a long time.

Direct:　He said, "I've been looking forward to meeting your family for a long time."

1. "I love zucchini," said Nino, "almost as much as I love peppers."

2. Bob told me that he was working in the library five nights per week.

3. "Roger has played a faltering but passionate cello for years," Erin opined with a grin.

4. Mary announced that she would be running in the Around the Bay marathon this year.

5. "Wait for the third quarter results," said the company spokesperson.

6. Annika observed that she had not seen many men in bikinis in beer commercials.

7. "Will the economy improve this year, Mr. Martin?" the anxious businesswoman asked.

8. The reporter asked the candidate whether or not she would vote for NAFTA.

9. "I may not have the money to travel home for Thanksgiving this year," Willy told me.

10. Whenever my grandmother found me working late, she would tell me that two hours at night were worth one hour in the morning.

ESL 6d, Conditional Sentences

Correct the verbs in the following conditional sentences.
For example: When air warms, it will rise.
Correction: When air warms, it rises.

1. If he sees a shooting star, he will make a wish.

2. If you practise enough, you could join a band.

3. If I had practised more, I may have my own band.

4. Wherever Fleetwood Mac performed last year, they find big audiences.

5. If the tornado had touched down, what damage would it do?

6. If you were the laboratory's teaching assistant, what will you do?

7. Whenever I have trouble sleeping, I will drink some warm milk and go right back to bed.

8. If I get lost on the way to the airport, I would miss my plane.

9. When I exercise at least three days per week, my back will never bother me.

10. Unless I hear from him today, I am assuming he is coming tomorrow.

ESL 7, Confusing Words and Phrases

Correct the following sentences, which contain words and phrases often confused and misused in English.

For example: After six hours on the bus I was glad to hear Gloria say we were most there.

Correction: After six hours on the bus I was glad to hear Gloria say we were almost there.

1. "You look tired; may be we should go home now?"

2. When I past the library I remembered I needed to return a book.

3. On what base did you decide to enroll in this class?

4. Leo's street is quite and pleasant.

5. Annita said that this dessert was her especially favourite.

6. I came yesterday, also I leave tomorrow.

7. Dolly noticed immediately that everyone at her new job dressed rather formerly.

8. In a new country, you need to learn the costumes in order to understand people's behaviour.

9. "Can you remember me when it's time to leave?" asked JoAnn.

10. The stale bread was hardly to cut.

Chapter 5

SENTENCES

SENT 1a, Irrelevant Detail

Edit the following sentences to eliminate irrelevant detail.

For example: The author's second novel, nearly four hundred pages long, did not receive the widespread acclaim of her first.

Correction: The author's second novel did not receive the widespread acclaim of her first.

1. Marx said that religion is the opium of the people, which is, I think, a strong opinion.

2. Charles Dickens, who died in 1870, was a prolific author, working on up to three novels concurrently.

3. In the last seventeen months our Liberal, incumbent prime minister, when not discussing the budget, has announced during Ottawa press briefings plans to elevate several governmental posts to the rank of cabinet minister.

4. Last Thanksgiving Chuck walked to and from the museum where he saw the Matisse retrospective.

5. The trans-Canada highway system, originally constructed to ease travel between provinces, is now badly in need of extensive rebuilding.

6. Whenever the wind blows from the north, which is actually quite often, you can hear the windows in our apartment whistle.

7. The area between the Tigris and Euphrates rivers, once home to the Akkadians and the Amorites, is known as "the cradle of civilization."

8. Our class trip to Ottawa, which is sponsored each year by a number of local organizations, was fascinating.

9. My brother, who loves to read, was just elected captain of the basketball team.

10. When I read Davies' *The Manticore* it was during finals week and I enjoyed it.

SENT 1b, Illogical Constructions

Edit the following sentences to eliminate mixed or illogical constructions.
For example: The reason why the baby cried is because her diaper needed changing.
Correction: The baby cried because her diaper needed changing.

1. The new bridge, still under construction, will relieve the traffic it creates.

2. They chatted like two birds until they ran out of steam.

3. The triple chocolate cake, my favourite recipe, was always delicious.

4. My brother wrote me a letter last week and I read them two or three times over.

5. I don't know nothing about Wagner's opera Parsifal.

6. Beginning after lunch, the wind blew all day.

7. The coach gave us six new plays that was designed to confuse their defense.

8. Susan Aglukark, her songs always powerful, captured the spirit of the Inuit people.

9. On Green Up Day my whole class went to the local park's playground and cleaned them up.

10. The reason abortion is such a contentious issue is because many people have differing views that they are absolutely sure are correct.

SENT 2a, Subordination

Using subordination, rewrite each set of short sentences as one sentence.
For example: The day was dreary. We went fishing anyway.
Rewritten: *Although the day was dreary, we went fishing anyway.*

1. Bill and Metsa have dated for five years. They started in high
   school. They think they will get married next year.

2. Donovan Bailey is fast. He has a strong kick. His speed and kick
   won him a gold medal at the track and field championships.

3. Our university library has over one million volumes. It covers
   most areas of information in depth. It also has information that is
   up-to-date. I do most of my research there.

4. Heat the sauce over a low flame. Stir constantly. Be sure that the
   butter does not brown.

5. The tulips on Parliament Hill are beautiful in the spring. They
   were a gift of the Dutch people. They are lovingly maintained. A
   symbol of friendship between the two countries.

6. I meet Sala for lunch every Friday. I enjoy talking with her.

7. Kim studied all weekend for the exam. He was tired. He did well
   on the exam on Monday.

8. The sun was hot. The humidity was high. It had been this way for
   two weeks. John wouldn't even play baseball.

9. My mother is a Stones fan. My father is a Beatles fan. They are both diehards. They still argue over which group is better. I have to listen to these childish discussions.

10. My sister is tall. She is strong. She is a team player. She was elected captain of the volleyball team.

SENT 2c, Coordination

Using coordination, rewrite each set of short sentences as one sentence.
For example: The Canadian economy is very complex. The Bank of Canada has a difficult job.

Rewritten: *The Canadian economy is very complex, so the Bank of Canada has a difficult job.*

1. I had a lot of reading to do every day. I did not watch television at all for months.

2. I agree with many things Robert tells me. I argue with him when I do not.

3. My great uncle does not smoke. He also does not drink.

4. He likes classical music. He also likes country and western.

5. This rain is good for people. It is filling the reservoirs.

6. At the heart of brewing is yeast. It converts sugars to alcohol and carbon dioxide.

7. We grow a garden every summer. We eat fresh vegetables every day.

8. I generally agree with Professor Tellman's theories. I am still unsure about some of his research.

9. I can take the 7:10 train. I can catch the 7:20 bus.

10. Copernicus used astronomical instruments that are very simple by modern standards. Copernicus changed our whole concept of humanity's place in the universe.

SENT 3a, Emphasis

Rewrite the following sentences placing the most important words or phrases at the beginning or end of the sentence.

For example: With politicians who happily confuse deficit reduction with debt reduction, what is the chance that a balanced budget is something we'll ever see?

Rewritten: With politicians who happily confuse deficit reduction with debt reduction, what is the chance we'll ever see a balanced budget?

1. Phil told me that Hogan's party was a great success once the band got going and everyone began to dance.

2. Not heeding a winter storm warning can be a grave mistake in the Maritimes.

3. When I first heard the plan I was thrilled, but now I'm not so sure.

4. Pedro's new job is challenging, so he's glad he took it.

5. *Carmen*, which Luis has seen eight times, is his favourite opera.

6. Erica was shocked by the calculation that $50 000 would be the cost of her college education.

7. The idea that love, for the most part, could overcome every obstacle was something Johanne believed.

8. In their discussions, the United Nations and NATO seem almost paralyzed with uncertainty about how to best handle Bosnia.

9. The new manager of our baseball team, Jim Jones, has been changing both the attitude and the motivation of our players.

10. A rattlesnake's bite is rarely fatal if the victim knows what to do.

SENT 3b, Logical Order

Rewrite each of the following sentences to improve its logical and/or climactic sequence.

For example: Franco passed the bar exam, studied hard, and was hired by a prestigious law firm.

Rewritten: Franco studied hard, passed the bar exam, and was hired by a prestigious law firm.

1. Margaret looked happily at the Seder table: the matzos, the single gold-rimmed cup of wine for Elijah, and the bitter herbs.

2. Carter had an awful day when we were at the Skydome; he struck out in the first, seventh, and fifth innings.

3. I like a movie if it has a good story, ends happily, and is well acted.

4. In the next three hours I need to dress to go out, shower and shave, and mow the lawn.

5. As I looked around the dimly lit attic, I saw dusty boxes, a complete human skeleton, and piles of old clothes.

6. After landing in Halifax, Marty picked up his luggage, drove into the city, and rented a car.

7. The thunderstorm raced in—lightning cracking and caroming, wind rising, and rain coming down hard.

8. To set up a family budget first determine what, if any, you can spend, then what your income is, and last what your expenses are.

9. John began his research paper by reading on his topic, taking notes, and finding a topic.

10. I admire Matisse's fantastic sense of form and movement, his rich use of colour, and his brush work.

SENT 3c, Active Voice

Rewrite the following sentences to change the active voice to the passive voice, or vice versa.

For example: Fresh peas were loved by Julie. (passive voice)

Rewritten: Julie loved fresh peas. (active voice)

1. Mosquitoes, black flies, and chiggers bit Paul on his canoe trip down the Peace River.

2. The ball was hit deep to centre by Alou.

3. A new puppy was bought by the family.

4. Everyone in our dorm celebrated Kurt's birthday.

5. I was called by Patrick as soon as he returned to Montreal.

6. By whom was *The Stone Diaries* written?

7. Many refugees were examined by customs officers at Gander airport.

8. Angela was read *Alligator Pie* by her parents as a child.

9. Now Angela reads *Alligator Pie* to Rosauro every night.

10. Maya's report was praised by her boss.

SENT 4a, Sentence Variety 1

Rewrite the following sentences to eliminate the overuse of short, simple sentences.

For example: Darif had a great day. He was early for class. He got an A on his midterm. He received a birthday card from his parents.

Rewritten: Darif was early for class, got an A on his midterm, and received a birthday card from his parents—a great day.

1. It rained for a month. There was great flooding.

2. Quebec has a long winter. It seems shorter now that I ski.

3. My parents sang every Sunday in church for years. Last year they stopped. They miss it now.

4. Fly over any major Canadian city. Look out the plane's window. You will be shocked by the number of swimming pools you will see.

5. Anne gets up at 5 a.m. every day. She never misses her gymnastics practice.

6. A house has many main parts. It has a foundation. It has a frame. It has sheathing. It has internal systems, such as electricity and plumbing.

7. I heard René's newest album on the radio. It's another hit, I think.

8. Every morning I get up. I exercise. I shower and dress. I carpool to work.

9. Hume read an article about government waste. It made him feel frustrated.

10. A new mall was proposed. It raised many questions. One of them was whom would it benefit.

SENT 4b, Sentence Variety 2

Rewrite sentences A & B to begin with the structure indicated.

Given: Ali and Lynda walked in the park and forgot about all their cares for the evening.

Begin with a Gerund:

Rewritten: Walking in the park was Ali's and Lynda's way to forget about all their cares for the evening.

Sentence A: Ali and Lynda walked in the park and forgot about all their cares for the evening.

1. Begin with an infinitive:

2. Begin with a participle:

3. Begin with a subordinate clause:

4. Begin with a coordinating conjunction:

5. Begin with a prepositional phrase:

Sentence B: Samuel de Champlain discovered a great freshwater lake, and claimed it for France to please the king in 1609.

6. Begin with an infinitive:

7. Begin with a participle:

8. Begin with a subordinate clause:

9. Begin with a coordinating conjunction:

10. Begin with a prepositional phrase:

SENT 5, Misplaced and Dangling Modifiers

Rewrite the following sentences to eliminate the misplaced and dangling modifiers.

For example: Jim could see the fish jumping from the campsite.

Correction: From the campsite Jim could see the fish jumping.

1. Don returned the tools to Phil covered with grease.

2. Threatened with extinction, Fisheries and Oceans Canada wrote new rules for the Beluga Whale.

3. I saw him on the walkway painted green.

4. Young and inexperienced jobs were few and far between Jim discovered.

5. I wrote directions for my friend to the house.

6. Prized by many, Leon won the award.

7. I saw a big grouper with my mask and snorkel on.

8. It was so hot that I watched Shania Twain dressed only in my underwear in The Canadian Country Music Awards show.

9. I gave Dulla a book in the library written by Leacock.

10. I could see Stonehenge coming over the hill.

SENT 6, Parallelism

Rewrite the following sentences to improve their parallel structure.
For example: Planes and trains are usually on time, and buses are, too.
Correction: Planes, trains, and buses are all usually on time.

1. We will see Rufus on Tuesday, and then Wednesday we are going to see Tito.

2. While he could not swim, a life jacket was something he would not wear.

3. The jet stream has remained centred on Saskatchewan, and the rain continues to fall.

4. Parliament does not think enough about the individual citizen, and it forgets about personal responsibility.

5. As the sun rose, the moon was setting.

6. Our team is well prepared and has great equipment; our coach too is excellent, and we've had a lot of practices.

7. I see a great future ahead, while in the past our record has been admirable.

8. He wanted to be on the stage, but he knew neither how to act nor singing.

9. Is it better to stand fast on environmental policy than having a compromise in order to save jobs?

10. At the local gas bar she is the manager, and she is also our class valedictorian.

SENT 7, Sentence Fragments

Rewrite the following sentences to eliminate sentence fragments.
For example: He loves to fish. Also hunt and hike.
Correction: He loves to fish, hunt, and hike.

1. My little brother is 185 cm. And still growing.

2. My brother Todd swam in high school. And dove in college.

3. While on vacation I read two children's books. Mireille Levert's *Sleep Tight* and Ron Lightburn's *Waiting for the Whales.*

4. Last night I saw Neville at the student union; Molly, too.

5. When I saw the Mona Lisa in person. I was, to be honest, disappointed.

6. The city jobs bill was stalled in the provincial legislature. Which is unfortunate.

7. Snappy replies in a candidate's debate can win you votes. But they do not constitute governing.

8. I saw most of my family over Thanksgiving. Anne, Michael, Kate, and Maggie.

9. Gertrude is my closest friend. Even though she moved to Italy.

10. After summer, I saw Jean very little. By winter, not at all.

SENT 8, Comma Splices

Rewrite the following sentences to eliminate comma splices.
For example: I love to cook, I hate to diet.
Correction: *I love to cook, but hate to diet.*

1. The Boer War marked the first time Canadian troops had been sent overseas, historians say.

2. Professor Gerson has a pleasantly acid sense of humour, he quipped that the term *political ally* is an oxymoron.

3. I practise conga one hour every day, this has helped me improve a lot in the last year.

4. Spring in Vancouver is cool, many visitors wished they had brought warmer clothes.

5. I am a business major, studying economics will give me a useful background.

6. Picasso's work has been classified into periods, perhaps best known is his Blue Period.

7. It was raining lightly, we set off on the hike anyway.

8. My roommate reported that my old sneakers had begun to move on their own, he said they were a violation of international treaties banning the development of biological weapons.

9. I had never driven to Red Deer before, I missed my exit from Highway 2.

10. Kaitlin reads the newspaper every morning, she is much more knowledgeable about current affairs than I.

SENT 8, Run-ons

Rewrite the following sentences to eliminate run-ons.

For example: Mariah was very physically fit she worked out five days a
week.

Correction: Mariah was very physically fit because she worked out five
days a week.

1. We took a cab to the theatre we saw *Show Boat.*

2. I hope Fred will come over and help me with my car I need to adjust the carburetor.

3. It rained for twenty days straight I felt like escaping to the desert.

4. I know what a typeface is I'm not quite sure what a font is.

5. Agriculture is still one of Canada's leading industries it contributes to our trade balance with the rest of the world.

6. I saw Susan yesterday she looked great.

7. I think it's three o'clock do we have to leave now?

8. When I visited Nyla over the holidays, I met many of her high school friends they were very friendly.

9. Can you come here and taste this soup I need an opinion.

10. We trained the telescope to the south Saturn was clearly visible.

Chapter 6

WORD CHOICE

WORD 1a, Denotation

Replace the italicized word—used incorrectly—in each of the following sentences with a word that denotes the correct meaning. Then identify the part of speech and write a short definition for both the incorrect and correct words. Consult a dictionary if necessary.

Example: Albert Einstein's work was *ingenuous*.
Answer: Albert Einstein's work was ingenious.
ingenuous: (adj) naive
ingenious: (adj) clever and inventive

1. What are the *affects* of the new spending bill?

2. Even if you disagree strongly with him, please be *civic*.

3. Emile was a *vociferous* reader.

4. Sex education has helped many teenagers get factual information on *venerable* diseases.

5. Paul, carried away by the emotional appeal of his own argument, went off on a *tangible*.

6. In an effort to keep the peace talks going, the ambassador *shuffled* between the countries in contention.

7. This apartment is cold because its walls have no *isolation*.

8. My new car uses almost 50 percent less fuel than my old one; its engine is much more *proficient*.

9. The facilitator successfully *meditated* the dispute.

10. George is *libel* to come in here at any moment.

WORD 1c, General versus Specific Words

For each general word in the list, provide a specific example.

Example: emotions: happiness

1. transportation:

2. foods:

3. vegetables:

4. seasons:

5. holidays:

6. colours:

7. metals:

8. trees:

9. music:

10. birds:

WORD 1c, Abstract versus Concrete Words

Identify each word in the following list as either abstract or concrete.

Example: emotions: *abstract*

1. pretty:

2. justice:

3. leaves:

4. blue:

5. stars:

6. wood:

7. fast:

8. cake:

9. truth:

10. shoes:

11. paper:

12. bright:

13. fun:

14. rock:

15. tall:

16. new:

17. slippery:

18. wind:

19. music:

20. juice:

WORD 1d, Idioms

Correct the misuse of prepositions in the following sentences containing idiomatic expressions.

Example: I am concerned for your attitude.
Correction: I am concerned about your attitude.

1. The committee agreed with the plan.

2. Frieda left early so that she would be sure and get a good seat.

3. My niece insisted that Jell-O was superior than pudding.

4. Though we arrived early, we still had to wait on line.

5. The coach gave me some extra tips to help me try and improve my shot.

6. Their route was different than ours.

7. The House of Commons concurred with the Senate's resolution.

8. Jazz is Hector's favourite type of a music.

9. When dancing with a partner, try not to vary to the beat.

10. Water Street is parallel from Canal.

WORD 2a–b, Appropriateness

Rewrite each of the following sentences, substituting for the italicized word or phrase a more formal expression.

Example: Jagdish *took off* after work.
Answer: Jagdish left after work.

1. Reggie *couldn't stand* their new album.

2. Bryan *can't* come today.

3. The show was *awesome*.

4. Collecting stamps was Phil's *thing*.

5. If I have time, *I'll catch a bite* with you at noon.

6. What *stuff* did Professor Higgins *talk about* today?

7. K.C. said, "*Don't dis your sis.*"

8. When *I'm done, I'm gonna bop down* to Ridley's.

9. Rickie decided *to hang* in the library *til* I finished.

10. Ozzie *shot the breeze* with Harriet on the porch.

WORD 3, Bias in Writing

Rewrite each of the following sentences to eliminate sexist terminology.

Example: Suzanne Porter was the anchorman on our local news.
Answer: Suzanne Porter was the anchor on our local news.

1. Our forefathers showed great courage to leave their homelands and voyage to a new and often little-known country.

2. The mayor was swamped with questions from the newsmen.

3. The writing course was tailored to freshmen students.

4. Who's chairman of that subcommittee?

5. Of all creatures on the planet, man is the most intelligent and the most destructive.

6. My bag is so heavy that I hope the hotel has a bellboy.

7. My sister-in-law is a policeman.

8. The job was so big that Laura was not sure our department had enough manpower to complete the work on time.

9. The plane was full and the stewardesses had to hustle throughout the flight.

10. All the firemen in my town are volunteers.

WORD 4, Wordiness

Rewrite each of the following wordy sentences to make them concise and direct.

Example: Good, clear instructions eliminate, I think, a lot of possible confusion later.

Rewritten: Clear instructions eliminate later confusion.

1. I'd say that Tom was basically a point guard that can, when he's got to, play centre.

2. I thought that the test was really hard on account of the fact that we had to know in essence everything from the whole semester.

3. Due to the fact that there was bad weather in Winnipeg, Bill's two brothers, who were flying, were delayed and we had to wait at the airport for them for five hours.

4. The school band, which it seems to me obviously hadn't practised enough, couldn't even play the national anthem without mistakes.

5. Can you explain why it is that schools of fish, which live in the water, and flocks of birds that fly in the air, move as a single group with similar coordinated motions?

6. The trees on my street, which are of three different types, all change colour in fall at what I would estimate to be the very same time.

7. The mayor, who was popular and who was already serving his third term in office, was given yet another vote of confidence at the polls by the voting populace at election time.

8. In spite of the fact that Orlo, who is conductor of our orchestra, was late, the concert began virtually on time.

9. While everyone's point of view, and ideas, and feelings, must be taken into account and assessed carefully and thoughtfully, it seems to me that in the end the prime minister is kind of charged with the task of leading rather than evaluating.

10. Foster Hewitt for all intents and purposes was a great hockey broadcaster for the simple reason that he was spare with his use of words, and he will long be remembered for that.

WORD 5, The Dictionary

Use your dictionary to answer the following questions.

1. How many syllables are in *oblivious* and *obnoxious*? Write out both words and mark the syllable breaks.

2. Define *marathon* and explain the origin of the word.

3. What is the etymology of the word *lens*? What type of lens best exemplifies this origin?

4. What is the origin of the word *frankfurter*?

5. How many syllables are in *scrupulous*. Write out the word and mark the syllable breaks.

6. Check the etymology of the word *bait*. You will find that it is a particular form of a related word that is also found in English. What is that other word?

7. What are the two meanings of the noun *chamois*? What are the variant spellings of this word?

8. What is the origin of the name of the game *hop-scotch*?

9. How has the word *apron* changed over time? (Hint: What is faulty separation?) Give a similar word that did not undergo this same change.

10. What is it that makes a *March hare* mad?

WORD 6, The Thesaurus

For each word given use a thesaurus to find five or more synonyms and at least one antonym. Indicate the part of speech for your entries.

Example: probe

Answer: noun: investigation; inquiry; examination; exploration; research; scrutiny; study
verb: explore; delve; dig; penetrate
antonym: (noun) cover-up

1. beautiful

2. show

3. prise

4. document

5. industrious

6. riot

7. hot

8. consolidate

9. palpable

10. assure

WORD 7, Usage

Correct the errors in word usage in the following sentences.

Example: The Pulitzer Prize is a honour.

Answer: The Pulitzer Prize is an honour.

1. I thought we could leave, but Joe ain't ready to go.

2. Nicholas loved music of all types, while Lou was very particular.

3. Although I set out twenty tomato plants this summer, none have any ripe fruit yet.

4. The show which is on Channel 42 at 10 tonight should be very interesting.

5. Jason should of arrived by now.

6. I like all winter sports accept curling, which I don't even understand.

7. The traffic was so light that we had no problem getting their on time.

8. No one RSVP'd, so I have no idea whose coming.

9. Although not nearly as dramatic as what was discussed in the popular press, the decreasing ozone levels have nonetheless been linked to climactic changes.

10. Each year the ocean currents cut further into the beach.

Chapter 7

EDITING FOR GRAMMAR

EDIT 1a–d, Subject–Verb Agreement 1

Correct the errors in subject–verb agreement in the following sentences.
For example: The depth of all three ponds are unknown.
Correction: The depth of all three ponds is unknown.

1. The ticket, including dinner with dessert, a floor show, and dancing after, are only twenty dollars.

2. The smell of the ripening apples and pears attract bees to the orchard.

3. Neither my parents nor my brother want to try my latest culinary
   triumph—cranberry-tofu meat loaf.

4. The House's minority makes their voices heard.

5. High tides and wind creates dangerous conditions along the coast.

6. Fourteen aunts, uncles, and cousins, except for Gramma Gump,
   was coming to our cookout.

7. The new library, though it had no windows, were bright and
   pleasant inside.

8. Six loaves of bread is not enough for this group.

9. Smith, Ruggles & Cleary have been practising law for fifty years.

10. The House of Commons are on summer recess.

EDIT 1e–1, Subject–Verb Agreement 2

Correct the errors in subject–verb agreement in the following sentences.

For example: He was the first of the thirteen batters who was struck out by Martinez.

Correction: He was the first of the thirteen batters who were struck out by Martinez.

1. Anyone who study regularly will do better in school and enjoy it more.

2. All the explanations is inadequate.

3. None of my classes meet before 10 a.m.

4. There is, on a regulation baseball team, nine players.

5. Politics both fascinate and repulse him.

6. Newspapers that covers controversial issues must work hard to be fair.

7. *Trudeau and our Times* were written by Stephen Clarkson.

8. One of his pairs of pants are ripped.

9. Whether privatization will result in more efficient services are debatable.

10. *Data* are the plural of *datum*.

EDIT 2a–b, Principal Parts of Irregular Verbs

Correct the misuse of irregular verbs in the following sentences.

For example: When the thunderstorm came through, it awakened me.

Correction: When the thunderstorm came through, it awoke me.

1. If you bent the pipe more, I think it will fit.

2. After John set down, he pulled out a book and dozed off.

3. Having took the subway for years, I was not easily startled by unusual-looking passengers.

4. Paul took the dinner roast out at noon because it was froze.

5. Having digged the trench, the workers laid the new gas line.

6. I had wrote to him all summer, but he only replied with a single postcard.

7. When the bell rung, the lecturer began immediately.

8. Once the paintings were hanged, the artist relaxed and got ready for the opening.

9. Many flowers and wreaths are lain at the Cenotaph every November.

10. It was his favourite sweatshirt, so he wore it even though it was tore.

EDIT 2c, Verb Tense

Rewrite the sentence provided in the verb tenses indicated.

For example: John and I often go to the movies together.

Present Perfect: *John and I have often gone to the movies together.*

I go to the All-Star Game every year.

1. Present Perfect:

2. Present Progressive:

3. Present Perfect Progressive:

4. Past:

5. Past Perfect:

6. Past Progressive:

7. Past Perfect Progressive:

8. Future:

9. Future Perfect:

10. Future Progressive:

11. Future Perfect Progressive:

EDIT 2e, Verb Mood

Write, in the parentheses provided, the mood of the underlined clause. Then rewrite the sentence, changing the underlined clause to the mood indicated at the beginning of the second line. For example:

(   )   <u>Come home after practice.</u>

INDICATIVE:

First fill in the mood of the underlined clause: (imperative). Second, rewrite the sentence, changing the underlined clause to the mood listed at the beginning of the second line ("INDICATIVE"). Thus, the completed answer would look like this:

(imperative)   <u>Come home after practice.</u>

INDICATIVE: I will come home after practice.

1. (   ) Bob asked <u>that he come early today.</u>

   IMPERATIVE:

2. (   ) <u>If I were training harder,</u> I would be better prepared.

   INDICATIVE:

3. (   ) <u>Every night he reads until bedtime.</u>

   SUBJUNCTIVE:

4. (   ) Cheryl said, "<u>Hurry up or we'll miss the bus.</u>"

   INDICATIVE:

5. (   ) <u>I wished it were snowing,</u> but it was only raining.

   INDICATIVE:

6. (   ) Loki said <u>her voice was similar to k. d. lang's.</u>

   SUBJUNCTIVE:

7. (   ) Don asked <u>if the campers could settle down.</u>

   SUBJUNCTIVE:

8. (   ) Chris wished <u>he were able to work more often</u>

   <u>at Bowrings</u>.

   INDICATIVE:

9. (   ) <u>If it were up to me,</u> I'd change the policy.

   INDICATIVE:

10. (   ) "<u>Don't forget to pick me up, Berto!</u>"

    SUBJUNCTIVE:

EDIT 2f, Active and Passive Voices

Rewrite each sentence changing its voice (that is, rewrite sentences in
the passive voice in the active voice, and vice versa). Indicate the voice
used in your rewritten sentence.

Example: *Star Trek* is loved by millions of Trekkies.
Rewritten: (active) Millions of Trekkies love <u>Star Trek</u>.

1. Jamal mailed the letters after lunch.

2. The dinner was cooked by Dominique.

3. Jean Larose wrote *La Petite Noirceur*.

4. Regina saw the Blue Line bus.

5. The World Series is watched by many people who rarely watch
   baseball otherwise.

6. The hills were set aglow by the summer sun.

7. Horseback riding demands subtle athleticism.

8. Our guide called the tallest maple the "Mother of the Forest."

9. Their farm produces 10,000 litres of milk each day.

10. Canoes are usually paddled by two people.

EDIT 3a–c, Shifts 1

Correct the inappropriate shifts in person, number, tense, or mood in the following sentences. Indicate the type of shift you are correcting. For example: I played basketball at the Y for years. I like their courts.

Correction: I played basketball at the Y for years. I liked their courts.
(tense shift)

1. The United Nations' membership has grown steadily, and they add one or more new members nearly every year.

2. When I study, I will usually work for at least three hours.

3. Once people swim in this lake, especially in August, you never want to swim anywhere else.

4. My father works for 42 years; he retired last month.

5. I will take the train to Batoche; let's go on the 10:37 train.

6. Although one prepared for the storm, I was nonetheless scared by its ferocity.

7. It is crucial to study regularly and don't get behind.

8. Denise reminded me to be sure to come early so you could get a good seat.

9. When I asked Nando what the difference was between handball and team headball, he says he doesn't know.

10. I remembered his advice that one has to swing smoothly in order to hit well.

EDIT 3d–g, Shifts 2

Correct the inappropriate shifts in subject, voice, quotation (direct versus indirect), tone, style, or perspective in the following sentences. Indicate the type of shift you are correcting.

For example: I told them to come on over if you want to learn the new rhythms.

Correction: I told them, "Come on over if you want to learn the new rhythms." (quotation shift)

1. I went to the new restaurant on Elm Street, and we enjoyed the meal.

2. Newsprint recycling requires extensive sophisticated processing, such as the de-inking of paper and the handling of the heavy metals extracted—no piece of cake.

3. Arlene said that she had read an interesting story in *La Presse* and you should read it too.

4. Broken down, we sat until the Transit Commission sent a replacement bus.

5. The school's main entrance was an imposing series of granite steps and landings leading up to a pair of great carved oak doors. The hallways were dark and long.

6. When we met at the Java Joint, the film was our main topic of discussion.

7. The trees lining the avenue created a leafy canopy overhead that looked like a green river running through the heart of the city.

8. The folks at Agriculture Canada have the important task of regulating Canada's agricultural policies.

9. The point of diminishing returns was approached as Parliament continued to modify the budget.

10. If someone wants to learn to read faster and better, it can be done through practice.

EDIT 4, Pronoun Agreement

Correct the errors in pronoun-antecedent agreement in the following sentences.

For example: If someone calls, please tell them I'll call back in an hour.

The problem: *someone* is singular, *them* is plural. There are many possible solutions; here are two:

> If someone calls, please tell him or her I'll call back in an hour.
> (grammatically correct but somewhat awkward)

> If someone calls, please say I'll call back in an hour.
> (switch to the verb *say*, which doesn't require an indirect object such as *them*, *him*, or *her*.)

1. The faculty votes for their officers every October.

2. He needs to better train his dog Biff, which barks at the letter carrier every day.

3. Neither Mrs. Williams nor Mr. Williams remembered their birthday.

4. When Louisa and Hal come to visit, they always bring his and her dog.

5. Each player in the tournament took his turn at the table.

6. The orchestra will open their twenty-eighth season with tonight's performance.

7. Either the boys or you needs to mow the lawn today.

8. Nicole's brother that served in the Navy is going to marry my sister.

9. My father and mother had his and her favourite dinner—fresh trout.

10. If someone liked the book, I think he will love the movie.

EDIT 5, Pronoun Reference

Correct the vague or confusing pronoun references in the following sentences.

For example: Lisa told Eliza that her car sounded as though it needed a tune up.

The problem: Whose car needs a tune up, Lisa's or Eliza's? There are many possible solutions; here is one:

Lisa said, "Eliza, your car sounds as though it needs a tune up."

1. Last night Adrian saw eight deer on the Fifth Concession, which was unusual.

2. Professor Marilee Tecknor, who studies retroviruses and has isolated a new subclass, gave a lecture on them at our seminar.

3. Although I know that supply-side economics focuses on production, and demand-side economics emphasizes consumption, this has never helped me understand where my paycheque goes every week.

4. When the company demanded a cut in wages and benefits, they recommended a strike vote be taken.

5. When tours come through our town, they often stop at the Shelburne Museum, where you can see an extensive folk art collection.

6. The region offers both the mountains and the ocean, so they rarely wish to move anywhere else.

7. The highway was backed up all the way to the overpass, and it was unlikely to clear out for several hours.

8. Cormac McCarthy's *All the Pretty Horses* combines ample description with sparse dialogue and it creates a rhythm not unlike a rider's.

9. In the newspaper they said the show opens tomorrow.

10. Driving into Scarborough on my last trip which is near Toronto, I ran out of gas.

EDIT 6a–e, Pronoun Case 1

Correct the pronoun case errors in the following sentences.
For example: Which one is the mayor? The woman on the right is her.
Correction: The woman on the right is she.

1. Have you seen mine brother?

2. After taking the subway, Chuck and me went to the deli.

3. If it were up to Laura and I, we'd leave now.

4. The boss appreciated them working on Saturday night.

5. My sister said she would be going to visit our grandmother after visiting Susan and I.

6. Gloria and me are best friends.

7. Us winning the Tri-City Invitational made the whole school proud.

8. Her and me studied for the exam with Tom, Rico, and Zöe.

9. The president of the student council is him.

10. Because the package was addressed to she and I, we did not wait for my brother to get home before opening it.

EDIT 6f–i, Pronoun Case 2

Correct the pronoun case errors in the following sentences.

For example: Fritz likes to swim more than me.

Correction: Fritz likes to swim more than I.

1. Professor Mbutuze asked Dave and I to participate in the experiment.

2. Despite all his campaigning, the *Ottawa Citizen* reported that the incumbent was running stronger than him.

3. My sister, whom has incredible hearing when it comes to the telephone, yelled out from the shower, "Who is that call for?"

4. With two runners on, Cheryl and I, our best hitter came to the plate.

5. The victory will go to whomever crosses the finish line first.

6. The registrar required Donna and she to submit transcripts for their summer work.

7. My brother and I are avid readers, but he hasn't read as many books as me this summer.

8. Because it was a tie, the prize was given to two runners, Phil and I.

9. I forget her name, but the Governor-General's Literary Award went to whomever wrote the non-fiction work *Touch the Dragon*.

10. *The English Patient* was written by who?

EDIT 7, Adjectives and Adverbs

Correct the errors in adjective and adverb usage in the following sentences.

For example: Josh can swim real fast.

Correction: Josh can swim really fast.

1. Laura grew more and more happily as the semester progressed.

2. I think it's coldest today than yesterday.

3. The Canada Council is charged with administering this kind of literary awards.

4. He is doing good in pottery class.

5. With two of their starters on the disabled list, things look badly for the Montreal Expos.

6. The steadily increase in sales before the holidays was offset by their declining steadily for the six months after the holidays.

7. After eating a $9 "tub of popcorn" at the movies, Sam was feeling badly.

8. Dirk read so quick that he finished the assignment a day before me.

9. The characters seemed happily engaged, but unhappily married.

10. Even though Elaine was a healthy thirty-four-year-old who had always eaten good, each Thanksgiving her grandmother said she looked a little thin.

Chapter 8

PUNCTUATION

PUNCT 1a, The Period

Correct the errors in the use of the period in the following sentences.

For example: Dorothy asked me if was I aware that sit-ups could strain my back?

Correction: Dorothy asked me if was I aware that sit-ups could strain my back.

1. If you know the Latin meaning abbreviated by am and pm, you will find it easier to remember which one to use.

2. One of the experimental drugs being used to combat AIDS is A.Z.T.

3. I wondered if he knew what the initials O.P.P. stood for.

4. One of the most resounding scenes in all of Shakespeare is in *King Lear* V, iii.

5. Tintin's best friend is Capt Horatio Haddock.

6. Last December he was promoted to President at Kahrdif, Inc..

7. Has your teacher ever told you to avoid using *etc* in your writing?

8. When Bert graduates from medical school next month he will be Dr Umberto Baldi.

9. They live just off of South Main St, I think.

10. Will you please walk the dog before leaving for the day.

PUNCT 1b–c, The Question Mark and Exclamation Point

Correct the errors in the use of the question mark and exclamation point in the following sentences.

For example: When is he coming.

Correction: When is he coming?

1. Louis asked me which class I liked best?

2. Joyce said, "Do you know whether bus or subway is the better way to get to St. Clair Avenue from here."

3. As usual for this region, the weather was sunny!

4. Which route to Antigonish has less traffic, John wanted to know?

5. "Can I come too," my sister asked.

6. Rolf asked me, "What is the difference between a CD and CD-ROM."

7. Wow. This pie is fabulous.

8. Whose book is that.

9. "Is that your book," Lisa asked me?

10. I could not remember when they were coming?

PUNCT 2a–c, The Comma 1

Correct the errors in the use of the comma in the following sentences.

For example: I limbered up for twenty minutes and I went for a ten-kilometre run.

Correction: I limbered up for twenty minutes, and I went for a ten-kilometre run.

1. He worked hard yet he was not feeling tired.

2. As Felix watched the cat ate her breakfast of Tuna Delight.

3. Last semester I had Professor Roop for history which has always been my favourite subject.

4. Yawning Susan put down her book and went to bed.

5. My oldest brother Geoffrey usually comes for Thanksgiving.

6. My favourite gardening book, *Flowers, Shrubs and Trees*, was written by a well-known botanist last year.

7. In summer, I get up very early.

8. Driving in the Indianapolis 500 which is one of North America's premier races, was an immense thrill for Paul Tracey.

9. Taken together increased personal deductions and no increase in taxes forebode an even larger deficit.

10. Having gotten lost twice already Doug thought maybe it would be wise to ask for directions at the service station.

PUNCT 2d–g, The Comma 2

Correct the errors in the use of the comma in the following sentences.
For example: I need to go to the bookstore, the library and the registrar's.
Correction: *I need to go to the bookstore, the library, and the registrar's.*

1. The recipe specifically called for ripe, large, red tomatoes.

2. This fall Eliot was reading Chaucer, Shakespeare and Milton.

3. For this reason the committee voted to change the policy.

4. The trade surplus has declined this year unlike previous years.

5. Riding into a head wind can help you improve your cycling endurance, power and technique.

6. John was elected by his peers to lead the team, and therefore feels both honoured and pressured.

7. The cost of health care has increased for example at a rate that far outstrips inflation.

8. As the workweek has been shortened, productivity has increased not decreased.

9. Their new house on Willow Street is small square and energy efficient.

10. They will discover however that appeasement has historically achieved not resolution, but mere postponement.

PUNCT 2h–l, The Comma 3

Correct the errors in use of the comma in the following sentences.
For example: The enthusiastic audience called out "More! More!"
Correction: The enthusiastic audience called out, "More! More!"

1. I smiled and said "Yes I'll be there."

2. If you want to call Phil has a phone.

3. Our reservations are for Friday August 19 through Sunday August 28.

4. Luke called yesterday and said "Congratulations on your new baby."

5. Lonnie gave me a ride from Calgary Alberta to Winnipeg Manitoba.

6. After dinner check your answering machine for messages.

7. John is drinking water and Mary soda.

8. "Well please come in" said my father graciously.

9. The MP, from the Yukon, said their office had received more than 1400 letters in favour of the bill.

10. Let's go now that we're ready.

PUNCT 2m, The Comma 4

Correct the following sentences by removing unecessary commas.
For example: Maybe, you'll receive the letter today.
Correction: Maybe you'll receive the letter today.

1. John and his brother, watched *Road to Avonlea,* every week.

2. I drove, last week, to Fredericton, New Brunswick, to visit my best friends.

3. The critics panned the play, *The Quiet Canadian,* as slow and pretentious.

4. If I, were you, I would leave before rush hour.

5. The small, gold, locket was a family heirloom.

6. He shipped me a box, that contained four hundred yo-yo's, missing strings.

7. He liked team sports such as, hockey, lacrosse, and football.

8. Jobs, jobs, and jobs, was the theme of his campaign.

9. He came early, and left late, much to my surprise.

10. She loved to go to the museum, on Saturday, but he, preferred Sunday.

PUNCT 3, The Semicolon

Correct the following sentences by either adding or removing semicolons as appropriate. Some sentences may be correct as given.
For example: It was a cool, gray day, the beach was empty.
Correction: It was a cool, gray day; the beach was empty.

1. The drive from Whitehorse to Dawson was long; but I didn't mind; nor did my sister.

2. The rapid decrease in computer hardware prices has put pressure on software developers to do the same, nonetheless, they have resisted the trend for the most part.

3. Last year I saw *Jurassic Park,* which used extensive computer animation, *In the Line of Fire,* which showed electronically manipulated "historical" photographs, and *Until the End of the World,* which presented computer-driven dream exploration—technology is now both a major theme and tool of the film studios.

4. I was shocked when I drove the $20 000 car, it rode only a bit better than my current car, which has a book value of only $1500.

5. Although I support universal access to health care; I disagree with waste; providing access shouldn't eliminate the option of user fees.

6. He was my best friend; and because of this he was always welcome in my family's home.

7. There are many ways of obtaining money to start a small business; which include personal savings, borrowing from a bank, or putting a mortgage on your property.

8. We thought we'd visit John on the way; but we ran out of time and had to pass by without stopping.

9. My sister's letter from Chobe National Park in Botswana took fourteen weeks to reach me; the letter and the park she described were both full of wonders.

10. The rainfall for the month of August was only forty millimetres, however that was normal for the region.

PUNCT 4, The Colon

Correct the following sentences by either adding or removing colons as appropriate. Some sentences may be correct as given.

For example: Alastair counted up his Halloween catch; 38 candy bars, 7 different types of chewing gum, and miscellaneous fruit that he did not even bother to count.

Correction: Alastair counted up his Halloween catch: 38 candy bars, 7 different types of chewing gum, and miscellaneous fruit that he did not even bother to count.

1. I have passed along to my children one of my father's sayings, "When you borrow something, try to return it in better condition than you received it."

2. Scientists, in an effort to isolate what it is in food that makes most people evaluate it as "tasting good or delicious," have determined the single most important ingredient, fat.

3. On your way home could you pick up: a kilogram of cold cuts, a head of lettuce, and a video.

4. Today is a very good day for haying; plenty of sunshine, a light breeze, and low humidity.

5. We took the following route, Highway 80 to Rock Springs, Highway 187 to Farson, and Highway 28 to South Pass City.

6. He speaks four languages, English, French, German, and Spanish.

7. Many vegetarians have a curious blind spot. They don't seem to realize that plants are just as alive as animals.

8. Mr. Thomason argued that there was one reason I failed the assignment, I didn't hand it in on time.

9. My aunt is fond of quoting from the Bible and regularly recites Luke 1, 2.

10. The Great Lakes include: Huron, Ontario, Michigan, Erie, and Superior.

PUNCT 5, The Apostrophe

Correct the following sentences by either adding or removing apostrophes as appropriate (and making any spelling changes necessary).

For example: Do you know the origin of the expression "Mind your *ps* and *qs*"?

Correction: Do you know the origin of the expression "Mind your p's and q's"?

1. We spent the day at Canadas Wonderland

2. My grandmother told me that the 38 hurricane was much worse than this years storm.

3. A snake sheds it's skin when its growing.

4. What is our companies policy regarding maternity leave?

5. I thought it was her's, but perhaps its really Bills.

6. I really enjoyed the Lions win over the Rough Rider's.

7. Oy! Jon's and Emily's dog, Bumper, has knocked over our garbage again. Now I know why thats his' name.

8. He accepted the managers recommendation.

9. Until this semester I had never used Petersens's Theory.

10. The teachers union and our school board seemed forever in negotiation.

PUNCT 6, Quotation Marks

Correct the following sentences by either adding, altering, or removing quotation marks and related punctuation as appropriate.

For example: O. Henry's short story The Gift of the Magi was included in his first book of stories, "The Four Million."

Correction: O. Henry's short story "The Gift of the Magi" was included in his first book of stories, <u>The Four Million</u>.

1. "Where you place your commas is one of my teacher's "things", so I always doublecheck my work", said Elaine.

2. "Would you like to come to dinner with us"? Mary asked.

3. When I read computer magazines I find all the technobabble confusing: "RAM," "ROM" and "bytes"—who dreams up these terms?

4. Milan told me that "he had written his term paper in just two hours."

5.   "I hope you'll come to our party tonight, said Alison.

   "Me too, I replied. "but I have to work until 11."

   "That's no problem; she said. It doesn't even start until 10, and I doubt you'll miss anything. Just come as you are after work.

6. Last year when I reread *The Canadian Charter of Rights and Freedoms*, I discovered it was much more interesting than I ever remembered it to be.

7. Ryan's research paper for English 101, The Changing Status of Euthanasia in Canada, helped him clinch an "A" in the course.

8. Punctuation is one of the chapters in "The Writer's Brief Handbook."

9. The proceeds go to a worthy cause, the "Jaime. L. Barzenté Memorial Fund."

10. "Where's the power switch,"? said Tom, as smoke poured from his computer.

PUNCT 7, Other Punctuation

Correct the punctuation errors involving the use of the dash, parentheses, brackets, ellipses, and the slash in the following sentences.

For example: Batman and Robin; also known as the "dynamic duo"; have been popular with three generations.

Correction: Batman and Robin—also known as the "dynamic duo"—have been popular with three generations.

1. One awkward, but acceptable, solution to the problem of sexism in pronouns is the use of *him, her* as well as *he or she.*

2. When in Rome (as the saying goes) do as the Romans.

3. The snowmobile known to many as the Skidoo was invented in Canada by Armand Bombardier.

4. "Our class meets in that new science building. What's its name? Something Hall . . . . Burstein . . . . Gurstein? I can't remember," said John.

5. I still remember the opening lines to Shakespeare's Sonnet LXXIII:

   "That time of year thou mayst in me behold

   When yellow leaves, or none, or few, do hang

   Upon those boughs which shake against the cold."

6. Leave now? We just got here—

7. The Red's starting pitcher, my neighbour's son, Jason, wound up and delivered a fastball.

8. I was happy I had voted for him, until he actually won the election.

9. The lecture, a ninety-minute torrent of anecdotes, facts, figures, and numerous slides, left me exhilarated but exhausted.

10. John switched his horses to compressed alfalfa from locally grown hay. Too often it caused colic.

Chapter 9

MECHANICS

MECH 1a–d, Capitals 1

Correct the errors in capitalization in the following sentences.
For example: Last Fall we hiked in the nechako range.
Correction: Last fall we hiked in the Nechako Range.

1. Unfortunately, stargazers living this far North can't see the southern cross.

2. When Tom "tiny" Anderson sang last week at the 3rd avenue grill, the crowd roared its approval.

3. The Cold War may be over, but we're still paying the bill.

4. The baptist church in my town sponsors a Community food shelf.

5. In the last four months the fraser and ottawa rivers reached record flood levels, but the liard river was below normal.

6. I sat late into the night with my family to see Neil Armstrong walk on the moon on july 20, 1969, during the *apollo 11* mission.

7. Last quarter the Royal and Toronto-Dominion Banks reported increased profits, while the National Bank profits were up only slightly.

8. My cousin Lou-Lou is the Founder of cara, the committee against ridiculous acronyms.

9. Once labour day weekend rolls around, you know that Summer is really over.

10. My Mother is a protestant, and my Father, a muslim.

MECH 1e–k, Capitals 2

Correct the errors in capitalization in the following sentences.

For example: When the storm came through, the weather turned cold. no, it became bitter.

Correction: When the storm came through, the weather turned cold. No, it became bitter.

1. In a recent article, economist Roy Brown wrote, "for the first time in our history, by the year 2000, fifty percent of all Canadian jobs will require at least one year of college."

2. I read the *Welland tribune* every day to keep up on local news.

3. During the Spring Semester I am going to enroll in Calculus, History, and English.

4. I think she bought one of the new Apple Notebook Computers.

5. Who reports on the News Media? the News Media does.

6. Have you read Judith Thompson's *the other side of the dark*?

7. Our city has two Mosques, four Temples, and twenty-eight Churches of various denominations.

8. Ford Trucks outsell all other makes in the maritimes.

9. During my first Semester at the university of Saskatchewan, I was swamped with work, but very happy.

10. In what year did Berton write *the national dream*?

MECH 2, Abbreviations

Correct the errors in the use of abbreviations in the following sentences.
For example: Laura's commission on new sales was 8 pct.
Correction: Laura's commission on new sales was 8 percent.

1. He reported to Sgt. Preston.

2. The prime minister announced that the new policy was designed
   to protect our natl. energy program.

3. Aristotle was born in B.C. 384.

4. Dr. James Wrinton, M.D. gave the keynote address.

5. For the trip they packed clothes, food, games, etc.

6. The dissolution of the Soviet Union has generated much debate
   over the future of N.A.T.O.

7. If we leave now, we'll get home in the p.m.

8. When people claim that electric cars are pollution-free, i.e., emit
   no pollutants, they forget one important fact: the power plant that
   generated the electricity used by the car isn't pollution-free.

9. Do you know the topic of Prof. Montrose's lecture for our 9 am
   seminar?

10. British and Canadian English differ in many small ways; e.g., we
    place a period after the abbreviation for *Mister* (Mr.), whereas the
    British do not.

MECH 3, Numbers

Correct the errors in use of numbers in the following sentences.
For example: Devon was born in nineteen seventy-one.
Correction: Devon was born in 1971.

1. Armand cut the plank into four two-metre sections.

2. Marc Garneau became the 1st Canadian in space aboard the shuttle *Challenger* on Oct. 5th, 1984.

3. Skosh thought the cost of the ferry ride was more than $20.00.

4. British Columbia has more than one thousand nine hundred elementary and secondary schools.

5. Over the holidays we saw four films, two plays, and 13 videos.

6. The competition was very close: only 1/8 of a second separated the 6 sprinters.

7. At the beginning of the 20th century, individuals travelled largely by horse; now we drive cars. What will we be doing at the end of the 21st century?

8. The final score was Tigers eight, Panthers two.

9. In 1993, Canada's budget for health care was over 72 000 000 000 dollars.

10. We got up at seven a.m. and swam before breakfast.

MECH 4, Italics/Underlining

Correct the following sentences by adding or removing italics as appropriate. Remember to indicate italics with continuous underlining (such as this sample).

For example: John told me to check The Cambridge Encyclopedia of Language.

Correction: John told me to check <u>The Cambridge Encyclopedia of Language</u>.

1. Linda likes Microsoft Word, but I prefer Claris MacWrite.

2. The most commonly occurring word in English is the.

3. I asked him to explain what noblesse oblige means.

4. Did you read last week's cover story in Saturday Night?

5. Tina asked if he would like a glass of *chablis*.

6. They rode Canadian National's Scotian from Montreal, Quebec, to Halifax, Nova Scotia.

7. Canadian-born William Shatner starred in the Star Trek television series and movies of the same name.

8. Hockey Night in Canada first went on the air in 1952, and continues to be Canada's longest-running television program.

9. His class is reading Dante's Divine Comedy in parallel texts—English and Italian.

10. Unable to travel, he was awarded the Nobel Prize in absentia.

MECH 5, The Hyphen

Correct the following sentences by either adding or removing hyphens as appropriate.

For example: His one year old car still looked brand-new.

Correction: His one-year-old car still looked brand new.

1. I am very close to my brother in law.

2. The ex Varsity halfback joined our club and boosted our whole team.

3. Are you looking forward to the beginning of the school-year?

4. Our class voted twenty one to seventeen for more study time.

5. In pre Confederation Canada many people lived on farms.

6. The police officer told me that J walking was illegal in this town.

7. The groom nearly fainted when the best-man couldn't find the wedding ring.

8. The premier elect will face many difficult issues this year.

9. When I was a thirteen year old, I played a lot of base-ball.

10. From the eighteenth- to the twentieth-century, the West has evolved from a pre industrial society to a post industrial one.

MECH 6a, Words that Sound Alike

The following sentences contain homophones used in error. Replace the incorrect word in each sentence with its correct sound-alike.

For example: After much deliberation, he decided to except their job offer.

Correction: After much deliberation, he decided to accept their job offer.

1. In our library, cereal acquisitions is on the 3rd floor.

2. In the 100-metre finals, Sarah was third and I was forth.

3. My father is sight manager for the new Deeter Building construction project.

4. My teacher recommended that we always read the forward, as it usually defines the scope and approach of the book that follows.

5. All the people I know with personal stationary are of my parents' generation.

6. When the passed president of the CAW addressed our school, he complemented the province's new labour relations policy.

7. If their coming with us, they have too hurry up.

8. I would rather work now, finish the reading, and than go to the late show.

9. Whose playing against the Canucks tonight?

10. The teenage years can be a period of extreme pier pressure.

MECH 6b, Basic Spelling Rules

Correct the spelling errors in the following sentences by applying the basic spelling rules.

For example: I beleive that he'll be over by eight o'clock.

Correction: I believe that he'll be over by eight o'clock.

1. I'm hopeing we can see Jeri before she leaves.

2. Professor Guimard is very knowledgable about plate tectonics.

3. Lofti Zadeh was lying down thinking when an idea suddenly occured to him; half an hour later he had laid out all the fundamentals of the feild now known as Fuzzy Logic.

4. How much did you say you payed for those peachs?

5. I sent the package via Express, so he ought to recieve it by noon tomorrow.

6. No sooner had the city finished paveing our street than the Water Department tore it back up again.

7. I love my brother, but I still think he's wierd.

8. These days, most people don't bother to pick up pennys.

9. It might sound odd, but our paper has two editor-in-chiefs.

10. We spend a lot of time with our nieghbours.

MECH 6c, Commonly Misspelled Words

The following sentences contain commonly misspelled words. Correct the errors in spelling.

For example: What's the difference between an abreviation and an acronym?

Correction: What's the difference between an abbreviation and an acronym?

1. John's horse, like most quarter horses, has a good temperment.

2. Parents frequently sacrafice for their children.

3. Our school has an excellent guideance counsellor.

4. What is your interpertation of these statistics?

5. I would like to go, wether Donna comes or not.

6. Her performance on the uneven paralel bars was extrordinary.

7. If you procede in this manner, you are probly going to have trouble.

8. Most corporations now have a practicle policy regarding the enviornment.

9. The ridges on that microprocessor help it disipate heat.

10. Morgage rates are currently at a thirty-year low.

Chapter 10

ESSENTIALS OF FORMATTING

FORMAT 1a–b, Basic Computer Formatting

A mock-up of a student essay is shown on the next page, and questions regarding this mock-up follow it.

Within the mock-up, lettered line segments mark a number of elements. For each such marked element, provide the appropriate margin or spacing. The first one is done for you as an example.

In addition, there are five formatting flaws in this mock-up. Using the spaces provided, list each formatting error and describe what should have been done instead.

(b)

(a)

Smith 1

(f)

    Lorem ipsum dolor sit amet, consectetuer adipiscing elit, sed diam nonummy nibh euismod tincidunt ut laoreet dolore magna aliquam erat volutpat. Ut wisi enim ad minim veniam, quis nostrud exerci tation ullamcorper suscipit lobortis nisl ut aliquip ex ea commodo consequat.

OGGETTI MAGGIORI

    Duis autem vel eum iriure dolor in hendrerit in vulputate velit esse molestie consequat, abitando

(c)

quest'anno in toscano. Vel illum dolore eu feugiat nulla facilisis at vero eros et accumsan et iusto odio dignissim qui blandit.

(e)

Punto Uno

    Praesent luptatum ril delenit augue duis dolore te feugait nulla facilisi. Lorem ipsum dolor sit amet, consectetuer adipiscing elit, sed diam nonummy nibh euismod tincidunt:

- laoreet dolore magna aliquam erat volutpat
- enim ad minim veniam nostrud
- exerci tation ullam corper suscipit
- lobortis nisl ut aliquip ex ea commodo consequat.

    Duis autem vel eum iriure dolor in hendrerit in vulputate velit essere molestie consequat, vel illum dolore eu feugiat nulla facilisis et tierne nog. Duis autem vel eum iriure dolor in hendrerit in vulputate velit esse molestie consequat, vel illum dolore eu feugiat nulla facilisis et tierne nog.

(d)

    (a) <u>top of page</u> to <u>last name/page number</u>: 1.25 cm (1/2 inch)

1. (b) top margin:

2. (c) left margin:

3. (d) bottom margin:

4. (e) right margin:

5. (f) linespacing:

    Formatting Errors:

6. --

7. --

8. --

9. --

10. --

FORMAT 2, Formatting Papers Using MLA Guidelines

A page of a student paper that should follow MLA guidelines appears on the adjoining page. Lettered line segments mark a number of elements on the page. Complete the following list by indicating next to each letter the appropriate margin, position, or spacing. The first one is done for you as an example.

In addition, there are six formatting flaws in this sample page; list them and describe what should have been done instead. Use the spaces provided.

    (a) <u>top of page</u> to <u>last name/page number</u>: 1.25 cm (1/2 inch)

1. **(b)** top and bottom margins:

2. **(c)** linespacing:

3. **(d)** left margin:

4. **(e)** right margin:

5. --

6. --

7. --

8. --

9. --

10. --

(b)

(c)

(a)

Lorem ipsum dolor sit amet, consectetuer adipiscing elit, sed diam nonummy nibh euismod tincidunt ut laoreet dolore magna aliquam erat volutpat.

OGGETTI MAGGIORI

Duis autem vel eum iriure dolor in hendrerit in vulputate velit esse molestie consequat, abitando quest'anno in toscano. Vel illum dolore eu feugiat nulla facilisis at vero eros et accumsan et iusto odio dignissim qui blandit.

(e)

(d)

Punto Uno

Ut wisi enim ad minim veniam, quis nostrud exerci tation ullamcorper suscipit lobortis nisl ut aliquip ex ea commodo consequat. Duis autem vel eum iriure dolor in hendrerit in vulputate velit esse molestie consequat, vel illum dolore eu feugiat nulla facilisis at vero eros et accumsan et iusto odio dignissim qui blandit praesent luptatum:

> "Delenit augue duis dolore te feugait nulla facilisi. Lorem ipsum dolor sit amet, consectetuer adipiscing elit, sed diam nonummy aliquam erat volutpat. Ut wisi enim ad minim veniam, quis nostrud aliquip ex ea commodo consequat."

Duis autem vel eum iriure dolor in hendrerit in vulputate velit esse molestie consequat, vel illum dolore eu

(b)

FORMAT 2, Formatting Papers Using APA Guidelines

A page of a student paper that should follow APA guidelines appears on the adjoining page. Lettered line segments mark a number of elements on the page. Complete the following list by indicating next to each letter the appropriate margin, position, or spacing. The first one is done for you as an example.

In addition, there are nine formatting flaws in this sample page; list them and describe what should have been done instead. Use the spaces provided.

    (a)   <u>top of page</u> to <u>last name/page number</u>: 1.25 cm (1/2 inch)

1.   **(b)**   top and bottom margins:

2.   **(c)**   linespacing:

3.   **(d)**   left margin:

4.   **(e)**   right margin:

5.   --

6.   --

7.   --

8.   --

9.   --

10.   --

11.   --

12.   --

13.   --

(b)

(c)

(a)

Lorem ipsum dolor sit amet, consectetuer adipiscing elit, sed diam nonummy. Nibh euismod tincidunt ut laoreet dolore magna aliquam erat volutpat.

OGGETTI MAGGIORI

Duis autem vel eum iriure dolor in hendrerit in vulputate velit esse molestie consequat, abitando quest'anno in toscano. Vel illum dolore eu feugiat nulla facilisis at vero eros et accumsan et iusto odio dignissim qui blandit.

(e)

(d)

Punto Uno

Ut wisi enim ad minim veniam, quis nostrud exerci tation ullamcorper suscipit lobortis nisl ut aliquip ex ea commodo consequat. Duis autem vel eum iriure dolor in hendrerit in vulputate velit esse molestie consequat, vel illum dolore eu feugiat nulla facilisis at vero eros et accumsan et iusto odio dignissim qui blandit praesent luptatum:

> "Delenit augue duis dolore te feugait nulla facilisi. Lorem ipsum dolor sit amet, consectetuer adipiscing elit, sed diam nonummy aliquam erat volutpat. Ut wisi enim ad minim veniam, quis nostrud aliquip ex ea commodo consequat."

Duis autem vel eum iriure dolor in hendrerit in vulputate velit esse molestie consequat, vel illum dolore eu

(b)

FORMAT 3, Formatting a Business Letter

A sample business letter by a student seeking employment appears on the adjoining page. Lettered line segments mark a number of elements on the page. Complete the following list by indicating next to each letter the appropriate margin, position, or spacing. The first one is done for you as an example.

In addition, there are eight formatting flaws in this sample page; list them and describe what should have been done instead. Use the spaces provided.

      (a)   top of page to top of return address: 6-12 linespaces (use this variation to balance the letter visually on the page from top to bottom)

1. **(b)**   linespacing:
2. **(c)**   left margin;
3. **(d)**   bottom margin:
4. **(e)**   right margin:
5. appropriate letter type (full block; modified block; indented)?

6. --

7. --

8. --

9. --

10. --

11. --

12. --

13. --

(a)

(b)

301 Electa Hall
University of Windsor
Windsor, Ontario   N9B 3P4

February 1, 1996
Mr. Harold Von Braun
Director, Managment Training Center
Acme Pyrotechnics, Inc.
Hamilton, ON L8N 3T2

Dear Mr. Von Braun,

(c)

(e)

Lorem ipsum dolor sit amet, consectetuer adipiscing elit, sed diam nonummy. Nibh euismod tincidunt ut laoreet dolore magna aliquam erat volutpat.

Duis autem vel eum iriure dolor in hendrerit in vulputate velit esse molestie consequat, abitando quest'anno in toscano. Vel illum dolore eu feugiat nulla facilisis at vero eros et accumsan et iusto odio dignissim qui blandit.

Ut wisi enim ad minim veniam, quis nostrud exerci tation ullamcorper suscipit lobortis nisl ut aliquip ex ea commodo consequat. Duis autem vel eum iriure dolor in hendrerit in vulputate.

Velit esse molestie consequat, vel illum dolore eu feugiat nulla facilisis at vero eros et accumsan et iusto odio dignissim qui blandit praesent luptatum.

Ut wisi enim ad minim veniam.

Sincerely Yours

William C. Aiote

William C. Aiote

Encl. Resume

(d)

Chapter 11

THE LIBRARY

LIB 1-4, Library Resources

Complete the crossword puzzle which begins on the next page.
All the answers correspond to various resources available in the library
to assist you in conducting research.

Down

2. Used to locate books within the stacks.
3. Acroynm for Compact Disc, Read-Only Memory.
4. Good source of geographical information, especially maps.
5. Abbreviation most often used when referring to the World Wide Web.
6. Most authorative historical dictionary of the English language.
7. Opposite of online.
8. General term for magazines, journals, and newspapers.
9. One of these typically contains information that is updated every year.
11. Name of the world-wide network of computers sharing information on almost every conceivable subject.
14. Another term for a summary of a book or article.
16. One of the three ways in which card catalogue information is organized.
18. A search by _____ in an electronic card catalogue can greatly increase the scope and possibilities of your search.
20. Software program used to look for information (files) on the Internet.

Across

1. Generally an excellent first resource for a topic new to you.
5. Source of brief biographical sketches on contemporary Americans.
10. Author of a very useful guide to the guides.
12. Best known guide to popular periodical literature.
13. Term meaning any store of information, typically large and accessed by computer.
15. Abbreviation for a four-volume reference that is essential for determining whether or not you are searching for information efficiently and thoroughly.
17. Abbreviation used in the Library of Congress Subject Headings volumes to indicate that the headings shown are more specific than your topic.
19. Principal tool for finding books within the library; formerly only a physical resource, now often an online resource (U.S. spelling).
21. Listing of books, articles, and other materials on a particular topic; often located at the end of an article or book.
22. Type of software used to access World Wide Web sites; Mosaic is one of the most widely used of these.
23. One of the three ways in which card catalogue information is organized.
24. Though most often used to find information on words, there are many different types of these.

Chapter 12

THE RESEARCH PAPER

RESCH 4b, Integrating Quotations

Quotations are generally used either to argue for or against an idea already presented in your paper. For each of the quotations provided below, write a paragraph that uses the same quotation to argue *for* an idea (pro) or *against* a idea (con). Or, your instructor may ask that you use the same quotation to write both pro and con paragraphs—as shown in the example below.

Be sure to use a clear signal phrase (author name, authority, and a carefully chosen introductory verb—such as "supports," "counters," etc.). Such signal phrases (1) help integrate the quotation smoothly into your own line of argument, (2) help your reader understand for what purpose the quotation is being used, and (3) help your reader distinguish your own thoughts from those of your quoted source.

For example:

Quotation and source: "The size of the 'hole' in the ozone layer would amaze most citizens." *The 1996 Annual Review of the Environment,* Peter Cannis, Director, Center for Atmospheric Study

"For" Paragraph:

The steady diminution of the ozone layer has caused the appearance of a vast area of thinning most often referred to a "hole." Many scientists are concerned that the general populace is too little concerned and informed about the problem. Dr. Peter Cannis, Director of the Center for Atmospheric Study warned, "The size of the hole in the ozone layer would amaze most citizens" (47). It is, in fact, the size of North America.

"Against" Paragraph:

The steady diminution of the ozone layer has caused the appearance of an area of thinning often referred to in the popular press as a "hole." Many scientists are concerned that the general populace has been falsely alarmed by vague and exaggerated claims. Dr. Peter Cannis, Director of the Center for Atmospheric Study counters, "The size of the 'hole' in the ozone layer would amaze most citizens" (47). It represents, in fact, only four percent of the earth's surface.

1. Quotation and source: "Many Canadians are of the opinion that citizens who have been unjustly treated by the government deserve some form of monetary compensation or, at the very least, an official apology." Christopher Dafoe, *The Beaver*.

"For" Paragraph:

_____

_____

_____

_____

_____

_____

_____

_____

_____

"Against" Paragraph:

_____

_____

_____

_____

_____

_____

_____

_____

_____

_____

2. Quotation and source: "Teaching etiquette is the kindest thing you can do for your child. It predates law and everything else in getting along with other people. You can't get away without etiquette any more than you can decide not to use language." Shelby Siems, *Christian Science Monitor*

"For" Paragraph:

_____

_____

_____

_____

_____

_____

_____

_____

_____

"Against" Paragraph:

_____

_____

_____

_____

_____

_____

_____

_____

_____

_____

3. Quotation and source: "In the classrooms of the future, teachers and textbooks could take a back seat to a revolutionary new technology that lets students experience the sensation of the lesson—holding a molecule, perhaps, or walking on a famous battlefield of the past . . . virtual reality." D'Arcy Jenish, *Maclean's*

"For" Paragraph:

_____

_____

_____

_____

_____

_____

_____

_____

_____

"Against" Paragraph:

_____

_____

_____

_____

_____

_____

_____

_____

_____

4. Quotation and source: "Like a great hive buzzing and building incessantly, Western Civilization has created a complex, organic home for itself: strong yet built of paper; vast yet composed only of small cells; and peopled by drones perilously dependent on a queen." Kaitlin Annah, *Biology as a Metaphor and Tool*

"For" Paragraph:

_____

_____

_____

_____

_____

_____

_____

_____

_____

"Against" Paragraph:

_____

_____

_____

_____

_____

_____

_____

_____

_____

_____

_____

5. Quotation and source: "It may be that as much was gained as was lost by the invention of writing. For although memory became more permanent by becoming encoded, and became transmissible across time and space, the performance aspect—the human dynamic between teller and hearer—fell darkly to the wayside, eclipsed by bare words, inanimate on the page." Bortollo di Fruili, *Art, Memory, and Performance*

"For" Paragraph:

_____

_____

_____

_____

_____

_____

_____

_____

_____

"Against" Paragraph:

_____

_____

_____

_____

_____

_____

_____

_____

_____

_____

RESCH 4d, Avoiding Plagiarism

For each of the quotations provided write an acceptable paraphrase, that is, one that avoids plagiarism. Pay particular attention to the word choice and sentence structure of the original.

1. "Some 2.4 million Canadian households—or 23 percent of the total—now have at least one personal computer. A growing number of those households also have a modem: a paperback-size device that allows a computer to be connected to networks via phone lines. About 30 000 Canadians use two of the country's largest on-line services—Toronto-based CRS Online and the National Capital FreeNet." (after Mark Nichols, *Maclean's*)

_____

_____

_____

_____

2. "All light sources emit waves uniformly in all directions. The amplitude of the waves is perceived by the eye as brightness, or luminance. In space the light waves from stars travel unimpeded and their self-propagating quality perpetuates them infinitely." (after Jeff Burger's *Desktop Multimedia Bible*)

_____

_____

_____

_____

3. "The sperm whale is the largest of the toothed whales. Moby Dick was a sperm whale. Generally, male toothed whales are larger than the females. Female sperm whales may grow 35 to 40 feet (about 10 to 12 metres) in length, while the males may reach 60 feet (about 18 metres)." (after Richard Hendrick et. al.'s *The Voyage of the Mimi*)

_____

_____

_____

_____

4. "Canada's Immigration and Refugee Board (IRB) grants refugee status to about 70 percent of those seeking asylum. That acceptance rate is about four times the norm for developed countries. The only way to hit a mark that high is to award refugee status to thousands who should not qualifty for it." (after Daniel Stoffman, *Saturday Night*)

_____

_____

_____

_____

_____

_____

_____

5. "Every one of Canada's 855 public general hospitals either is going, has gone or is about to go through the same thing at the hands of a deficit-plagued provincial government. The health-care system is an enormous target for budget cutters; in 1993 it cost roughly $70 billion, ten percent of gross domestic product, around $2500 per capita." (after Rae Corelli, *Maclean's*)

_____

_____

_____

_____

_____

_____

_____

6. "Astronauts from over twenty nations have gone into space and they all come back, amazingly enough, saying the very same thing: the earth is a small, blue place of profound beauty that we must take care of. For each, the journey into space, whatever its original intents and purposes, became above all a spiritual one." (after Al Reinhert's *For All Mankind*)

_____

_____

_____

_____

7. "What is technophobia really about? It's not an unhealthy and unjustified fear of confusing machinery that may break, bringing potential embarassment or worse. No, it's a natural reaction to poorly designed machines." (after Donald Norman's *Defending Human Attributes in the Age of the Machine*)

8. "One of the usual things about education in mathematics is its relatively impoverished vocabulary. Whereas the student completing elementary school will already have a vocabulary for most disciplines of many hundreds, even thousands of words, the typical student will have a mathematics vocabulary of only a couple of dozen words." (after Marvin Minsky's *The Society of Mind*)

9. "Underlying all great works of art is the artist's completely private and unfathomable tenacity—his or her unrelenting pursuit of an idea, a feeling, or a vision beyond the boundaries where most of us would stop. Travelling into places beyond our ken, they return with artifacts that we can inspect in the safety of a gallery or

museum. But just as we don't mistake a trip to the natural history museum for a visit to the jungle itself, nor should we mistake a visit to an art museum for the creative ferment of the artist's studio. The gilt-framed museum painting, hung in front of speechless crowds shuffling respectfully past, is no more alive than the stuffed museum lion, posed with its false glass eyes mocking menace and forever unmoving. And if we turn to ask the artists themselves about these pieces? They are nowhere to be seen, for they are packed and already gone." (after Thomas Murphy's essay, "Private Experience and Public Display" in *The Collected Works of T. D. Murphy*)

_____

_____

_____

_____

_____

_____

_____

_____

_____

10. "In archetypal symbolism, clothing represents *persona*, the first view the public gains of us. Persona is a kind of camouflage which lets others know only what we wish them to know about us, and nothing more. But the persona is not just a mask to hide behind, it is also a presence which eclipses the mundane personality. In this sense, persona or mask is an outward signal of rank, virtue, character, and authority." (after Clarissa Pinkola Estés's *Women Who Run with the Wolves*)

_____

_____

_____

_____

_____

_____

_____

_____

Chapter 13

MLA STYLE DOCUMENTATION

MLA DOCU 1, MLA In-Text Citations

For each of the following exercises write a passage incorporating the quoted material and giving an MLA-style in-text citation. Use signal phrases as indicated.

For example:

Format:	Quote the following author using a signal phrase.
Author:	Giuliano Procacci
Quote:	"Yet it was not until 1930 that, for the first time in the history of Italy, the value of industrial production overtook that of agriculture."
Source:	*History of the Italian People*, page 379
Context:	This is the only document by this author being used.

Possible Answer:

Of the slow-coming industrialization of Italy, Procacci notes that "it was not until 1930 that, for the first time in the history of Italy, the value of industrial production overtook that of agriculture" (379).

1. | | |
    |---|---|
    | Format: | Quote the following author without using a signal phrase. |
    | Author: | Richard Adams |
    | Quote: | "Human beings say, 'It never rains but it pours.' This is not very apt, for it frequently does rain without pouring. The rabbits' proverb is better expressed. They say, 'One cloud feels lonely.'" |
    | Source: | *Watership Down*, fiction, chapter 23, page 184 |
    | Context: | This is the only document by this author being used. |

2. Format: Quote the following author using a signal phrase.

    Author: Richard Adams

    Quote: "Human beings say, 'It never rains but it pours.' This is not very apt, for it frequently does rain without pouring. The rabbits' proverb is better expressed. They say, 'One cloud feels lonely.'"

    Source: *Watership Down*, fiction, chapter 23, page 184

    Context: This is one of two documents by this author being used.

_____

_____

_____

_____

3. Format: Quote the following authors without using a signal phrase.

    Authors: Charles Heimler and Charles Neal

    Quote: "A cloud is a collection of water droplets or ice crystals in the air. It is formed when water vapor is cooled and changed into water droplets or ice crystals."

    Source: *Principles of Science*, page 234

    Context: This is the only document by these authors being used.

_____

_____

_____

_____

4. Format: Quote the following author using a signal phrase.

   Author(s): Charles Heimler and Charles Neal

   Quote: "A cloud is a collection of water droplets or ice crystals in the air. It is formed when water vapor is cooled and changed into water droplets or ice crystals."

   Source: *Principles of Science*, page 234

   Context: This is one of three documents by these authors being used.

_____

_____

_____

_____

5. Format: Quote the following author using a signal phrase.

   Author: Reginald J. Symington

   Quote: "NATO's muddled expansion is so fraught with competing strategies that it has simultaneously threatened Moscow and made overtures to Russia to join the alliance itself."

   Source: "NATO at the Crossroads," in *Foreign Affairs*, April 1996, page 267

   Context: This is one of two articles by this author being used.

_____

_____

_____

_____

6. Format: Quote the following author using a signal phrase.
   Author: Allen Ginsberg
   Quote: "I saw the best minds of my generation destroyed by madness / starving hysterical naked."
   Source: "HOWL Parts I and Part II," poem, lines 1-2
   Context: This is the only piece by this author being used.

---

7. Format: Quote the following author using a signal phrase.
   Author: Anne Tierney
   Quote: "Computers have only very recently become common outside narrowly defined locations such as academia, business, and the military. We have yet to see what the age of 'personal computing' will mean."
   Source: Personal Interview, 22 December 1995
   Context: This is the only document by this author being used.

---

8. Format: Quote the following authors without using a signal phrase.

   Authors: Alfred Rosa, Paul Eschholz, and John Roberts

   Quote: "A good prose composition, regardless of its length, is purposeful and well organized."

   Source: *The Writer's Brief Handbook*, page 1

   Context: This is the only document by these authors being used.

   _____

   _____

   _____

   _____

9. Format: Quote the following authors using a signal phrase.

   Authors: Alfred Rosa, Paul Eschholz, and John Roberts

   Quote: "A good prose composition, regardless of its length, is purposeful and well organized."

   Source: *The Writer's Brief Handbook*, page 1

   Context: This is one of three documents by these authors being used.

   _____

   _____

   _____

   _____

10. Format: Quote the following author using a signal phrase.

    Authors: Corporate Author, Solar United Now (SUN)

    Quote: "Solar power is rapidly becoming financially viable primarily due to increasing solar conversion efficiencies and improved manufacturing. It would in fact compete favourably now with coal and oil if it were not for those industries 'subsidies' in the form of federal policies, laws, and tax code provisions."

    Source: *A Solar Primer*, page 8

    Context: This is the only document by this author being used.

_____

_____

_____

_____

_____

_____

_____

_____

Chapter 14

OTHER SYSTEMS OF DOCUMENTATION

OTHER DOCU 2, APA-Style References

This two-part exercise is based upon the research process for a student preparing a paper that must follow APA conventions. You are supplied with a computer printout compiled by the student using an electronic card catalogue. Using this printout you are asked to do do two things:

(1) prepare bibliography cards; (Use the blank note cards provided.)
(2) compile these cards into a "References" section that incorporates all these cards into a *single* list. (Use a separate sheet of paper.)

Note that the computer printout *does not use* the APA conventions that you need to follow.

For example, given the following printout:

```
Francis, R. Douglas.
Destinies: Canadian History
Since Confederation. 3rd ed.
537 p. : index, biblio
Toronto, Harcourt, 1996
FC164.  F73  1996
```

You would create this APA-style bibliography card:

Francis, R. D. (1996). <u>Destinies: Canadian history</u>

<u>since Confederation</u>. Toronto: Harcourt

FC164
.F73
1996

And you would create this entry in your paper's References section:

Francis, R. D. (1996). <u>Destinies: Canadian history since</u>

<u>Confederation</u>. Toronto: Harcourt.

Card Catalogue Printout and Preliminary Bibliography Cards:

```
------------------------------
Proctor, George A.
Canadian Music of the Twentieth Century
Toronto: University of Toronto Press, 1982.
ML205.5   P76   1982
------------------------------
Garraty, Jon B., editor.
The Musical '50's. 324 p. : illus.
Chicago: University of Chicago Press, 1982.
MN248   .G12   1982
------------------------------
McCready, Louise G.
Famous Musicians. 140 p. : Illus.
Toronto: Clarke Irwin, 1957.
ML385   .M173   1957
------------------------------
Jameson, MaryBeth.
"A Blue Note Discography " in William Cantor and Bruce Derries,
eds.,  in A Fine Blue Note. 398 p.
Boston, MA: Thwickham & Burley, 1988.
MN438   .J21   1988
------------------------------
Ford, Clifford.
Canada's Music: An Historical Survey.
Agincourt, ON: GLC, 1982.
N205.1   .F67   1982
------------------------------
Bradley, Ian L.
Twentieth Century Canadian Composers n.p.
Agincourt, ON: GLC, 1977.
N390   .B8   1977
------------------------------
Guenter, Larry.
Up All Night: A History of the Blues. 420 p. : Biblio.
New York, NY: Melody Press, 1990
MN437   .G554   1990
------------------------------
Gutman, Stanley N.
The Music Business. 384 p. : illus. , biblio.
New York, NY: Phantom Press, 1977.
MN439   .G229   1977
------------------------------
McLaughlin, Gloria. "Uptown, Downtown: Jazz and Socioeconomic
Status"
The Journal of Musical History, 2. April 1971. 299-314.
------------------------------
Ray, Randy, and Mark Kearney.
Canadian Music Fast Facts: Profiles of
Canada's pop music pioneers. unpaged.
London, ON: Jefferson, 1992.
ML394   .C342   1992
```

SELECTED

ANSWERS

TO

EXERCISES

COMPOSING

COMP 5c, Proofreading—see your instructor

PARAGRAPHS

PARA 1, Unity

1. <u>Mental models, our conceptual models of the ways objects work, events take place, or people behave, result from our tendency to form explanations of things.</u> These models are essential in helping us understand our experiences, predict the outcomes of our actions, and handle unexpected occurrences. ~~Unexpected occurrences can happen at any time.~~ We base our models on whatever knowledge we have, real or imaginary, naive or sophisticated.

   [Source: modified from Norman, Donald A. *The Psychology of Everyday Things.* NY: Basic, 1988. 38.]

2. <u>The market is as much a part of your company as you are.</u> After all, it represents one-half of the ledger. To grow, your business must earn the permission of the marketplace. No concept is more important for the start-up entrepreneur. ~~Guarantees are an essential component.~~ The customer must give your business permission to sell to him. He does this (at least as a repeat customer) only after a thorough assessment of you, your product or service, and your operation. This is why Detroit is having trouble selling cars even though they're better built than they were. ~~Fortunately this hasn't been a problem in the U.S. aerospace industry.~~ These cars have to overcome years of bad notices. It will take time to accomplish this. In fact, it may take until there's a complete turnover in the market—until those of us who now think Japanese or German no longer drive.

   [Source: modified from Hawken, Paul. *Growing a Business.* NY: Simon & Schuster, 1987. 175-176.]

3. <u>A classical understanding sees the world primarily as underlying form itself.</u> <u>A romantic understanding sees it primarily in terms of immediate appearance.</u> If you were to show an engine or a mechanical drawing or an electronic schematic to a romantic it is unlikely he would see much in it. It has no appeal because the reality he sees is its surface. Dull, complex lists of names, lines and numbers. Nothing interesting. ~~Classification systems may say more about their creators than about the objects being classified.~~ But if you were to show the same blueprint or schematic or give the same description to a classical person, he might look at it and then become fascinated by it because he sees that within the lines and shapes and symbols is a tremendous richness of underlying form.

   [Source: modified from Pirsig, Robert M. *Zen and the Art of Motorcycle Maintenance*. NY: Bantam, 1974. 66.]

4. <u>At a certain season of our life we are accustomed to consider every spot as the possible site of a house.</u> I have thus surveyed the country on every side within a dozen miles of where I live. In imagination I have bought all the farms in succession, for all were to be bought, and I knew their price. ~~I enjoy walking and find it a healthful relaxation.~~ I walked over each farmer's premises, tasted his wild apples, discoursed on husbandry with him, and took his farm at his price.

   [Source: modified from Thoreau, H. D. *Walden*. Princeton: PUP, 1971. 81.]

5. As the rules of chess define the game of chess, <u>linguistic rules define the game of language, which would not exist without them.</u> They are not strict mechanism of cause and effect—one thing simply making another thing happen—but a system essentially open and incomplete, so that it is always capable of novelty. Rules of etiquette close off a system, keeping it uniform and predictable unless the rules are changed. ~~Who is allowed to changes these rules? When can such changes be made?~~ Rules of language are indirect and can be used again and again on the same finite set of letters and words, making possible an open universe of new sentences on the closed universe of the dictionary. ~~Dictionaries you will have noticed are printed, not spoken.~~

   [Source: modified from Campbell, Jeremy. *Grammatical Man*. NY: Simon & Schuster, 1982. 127.]

PARA 2b, Development Strategies 1

1. Donald Norman's *The Psychology of Everyday Things*:
   definition; cause and effect
2. Paul Hawken's *Growing a Business*:
   definition; examples
3. Robert Pirsig's *Zen and the Art of Motorcycle Maintenance*:
   definition; contrast
4. Henry David Thoreau's *Walden*:
   definition; narration
5. Jeremy Campbell's *Grammatical Man*:
   definition; examples

PARA 2b, Development Strategies 2

Many different strategies could be used, depending on the information you gather, your approach to the material, and your audience. Here are some possibilities:

1. definition; comparison and contrast; facts and statistics
2. definition; comparison and contrast
3. facts and statistics (to quantify recycling); cause and effect (to discuss the rate of adoption)
4. definition; cause and effect
5. comparison and contrast

PARA 3, Coherence 1—see your instructor.

PARA 3, Coherence 2—see your instructor.

PARA 3, Coherence 3—see your instructor.

GRAMMAR ESSENTIALS

GRAM 1a, Verbs

1. Tina <u>swims</u> in the pool on Tuesdays.

         Vi

2. John <u>gave</u> <u>Fred</u> <u>a birthday present</u>.

         Vt   IO   DO

3. The weather <u>seems</u> <u>fine</u> today.

                 VI   PA

4. Shelby <u>bought</u> <u>her textbooks</u> at the campus bookstore.

           Vt   DO

5. Jorge <u>is</u> <u>a tenor</u>.

         VI   PN

GRAM 1b, Nouns

	singular	plural	sing. possessive	pl. possessive
1.	dish	dishes	dish's	dishes'
2.	hero	heroes	hero's	heroes'
3.	book	books	book's	books'
4.	wife	wives	wife's	wives'
5.	man	men	man's	men's

GRAM 1c, Pronouns

1. <u>I</u> gave Donald a call.
2. <u>I</u> spoke to <u>him</u> yesterday.
3. <u>He</u> usually has to call <u>me</u> back.
4. Raspberries are ready at <u>their</u> farm.
5. <u>Which</u> farm, McGuire's?

GRAM 1d, Adjectives

1. If presented with Häagen-Dazs and Ben & Jerry's, could you say which is (creamy, _creamier_, creamiest)?
2. The _Edmonton Journal_ declined to name the (good, better, _best_) candidate amongst the five potential nominees.
3. Jack is (old, _older_, oldest) than his brother John.
4. Jack is the (old, older, _oldest_) of the four children.
5. Before starting the 108 riders, the judge called, "May the (good, better, _best_) cyclist win!"

GRAM 1e, Adverbs

1. John runs _fast_.
2. Of all the sopranos, Lena sang the _most beautifully_.
3. The commute home _always_ seemed longer than the one to the office.
4. After the thunderstorm, steam rose _eerily_ from the _still_ warm pavement.
5. Jackson was tired but worked _hard_ to finish the assigned reading before going to bed.

GRAM 1f, Prepositions

1. (_On_ the move) (_since_ dawn), the hikers had advanced thirty kilometres (_by_ lunchtime).
2. Sara finished three (_of_ the four essay questions) quickly.
3. Chu's nieces and nephews danced (_around_ the room).
4. Bill saw his token roll (_into_ the street) and disappear (_down_ a storm drain).
5. Forty-seven storeys (_above_ the street), the falcons built their nest (_on_ one (_of_ the building's gargoyles)).

GRAM 1g, Conjunctions

1. I went to the store (_before_ Sushmito arrived). (SUB)
2. It rained all night, (_so_ the tournament was postponed). (COORD)
3. I like to fish even (_though_ I don't catch anything most days). (SUB)
4. (_Although exercise_ is important), there are days when I prefer to just lounge around on the beach. (SUB)
5. Professor Stanley asked us (_not only_ to compare and contrast Laurence and Mitchell, _but also_ to use one or more of their works to support our points). (CORREL)

GRAM 2a, Subjects

1. <u>My dog</u> sleeps so much that my roommate thinks she's a stuffed animal.
2. <u>Ly's enthusiasm for our annual reunion</u> is infectious.
3. <u>Joan's track and swimming talents</u> earned her a scholarship.
4. <u>Calculus 201 and Chemistry 137</u> have kept me extremely busy this semester.
5. <u>The university</u> has five libraries.

GRAM 2b, Predicates

1. Smoking <u>is expensive and addictive.</u>
2. Jacques <u>believed that his studies were a worthwhile investment.</u>
3. Melissa's research paper <u>explored the differences between personal debt and the federal debt.</u>
4. Gwen <u>is the oldest of five children.</u>
5. Bill and Ted <u>cooked dinner together most nights.</u>

GRAM 3b, Verbals

1. I love <u>running</u> because it requires so little equipment. (GER)
2. <u>Pacing yourself</u> during an exam is crucial. (GER)
3. The drummer <u>playing the timbales</u> is my cousin. (PRES PART)
4. The rebel army, <u>faced with many hardships,</u> managed <u>to defeat</u> <u>the better trained and equipped enemy.</u> (PAST PART; INF; PAST PART)
5. <u>To conduct good science</u> requires first good <u>training;</u> second, good insight; and third, great effort. (INF; GER)

GRAM 4, Clauses

1. <u>When I saw Roger,</u> <u>who was just returning from a trip,</u> he told me <u>he would be playing softball with us this Saturday.</u> (ADV CLS; ADJ CLS; NOUN CLS)
2. Ceilia painted her house purple <u>because it was her favourite color.</u> (ADV CLS)
3. <u>If you hit or tip a ball foul and you already have two strikes,</u> the count remains unchanged. (ADV CLS)

4. He hoped <u>his contribution to the charity would benefit [whoever was most in need]</u>. (NOUN CLS [NOUN CLS])

5. After losing three games straight, the team was overjoyed <u>when it beat the undefeated first place team</u>. (ADV CLS)

GRAM 5, Types of Sentences

1. Though ink may look black, it also contains red pigment. (complex)

2. Fred likes to read in bed. (simple)

3. Blue Jays and Cardinals are examples of birds that remain in southern Ontario over the winter. (simple)

4. After scooping ice cream all summer, my right arm was so strong that I could beat my older brother in arm wrestling, and my left arm looked so withered to me that it seemed almost useless, like the forelegs of <u>Tyrannosaurus rex</u>. (compound-complex)

5. Though it may sound odd, I swim in the winter and ski in the summer. (complex)

ESL BASICS

ESL 1a, Modal Auxiliaries

1. In one hour I will be done.
2. You will see me there tonight.
3. I should be able to finish this novel before class.
4. We cannot come to the party.
5. When I was growing up, my family would usually take a trip in the summer.

ESL 1b, Perfect Tenses

1. They have travelled too much this year to want to go on another trip soon.
2. We had expected you yesterday.
3. Bill goes to the movies frequently; he will have seen that one already.
4. Chloë had sung in the choir for three years before she was chosen to be its director.
5. Suzanne has brought me flowers every year on my birthday.

ESL 1c, Progressive Tenses

1. John is seeing René for the first time.
2. Sheila is giving her friends dancing lessons.
3. The ozone layer has been thinning because of the release of CFCs.
4. Joanne is happy today.
5. Sanga had been thinking calculus was easy until he took the midterm exam.

ESL 1d, Passive Voice 1

1. The NHL championship was won by Montreal this year.
2. Africa is visited by many Canadians.
3. We were seated by the hostess.
4. Many books are now published only in paperback.
5. Every student is expected to do well in his or her studies.

ESL 1d, Passive Voice 2

1. Tom lost my backpack yesterday.
2. Every day many commuters see the memorial to Canada's armed forces.
3. Bizet wrote <u>Carmen</u>.
4. Many people enjoy reading.
5. My parents saved money scrupulously.

ESL 1e, Two-Word Verbs

1. Where's the newspaper? Oh, John threw it away?
2. The teacher called on the student.
3. Because of the extensive fire damage, the Fire Marshall ordered the building's owners to tear it down.
4. Simone heard from her best friend.
5. Why doesn't he pick on someone his own size?

ESL 1f, Verb Phrases

1. They agreed to come over here before the game.
2. Josef urged me to see the film.
3. The boss permitted me to take time off when my sister was married.
4. I imagine flying is wonderful.
5. When I finish eating, I'll read to you.

ESL 2a–c, Count and Noncount Nouns

1. Gordon knows a lot of local history.
2. How many loaves of bread did Orlo ask us to pick up? —or—
   How many types of bread did Orlo ask us to pick up?
3. Howard used two hundred pails of sand to build his huge sand castle.
4. Ryan said many machines are built there.
5. Don't put too much salt in the soup!

ESL 2d, Definite Article

1. [To the waiter:] May I have some ketchup please?

   [Later, when it's already on the table:] Please pass the ketchup.

2. Mount Logan is the highest peak in Canada.

3. I saw the professor who won the Nobel Prize last year.

4. Hockey is very popular here.

5. I saw Bob walking down the hall just a minute ago.

ESL 3a, Cumulative Adjectives

1. a long white pearl necklace

2. my first new bicycle

3. five small square buildings

4. an ancient brick fireplace

5. seven large triangular windows

ESL 3b, Present and Past Participles

1. Lola found the novel's ending surprising.

2. The winter winds here are very drying.

3. Sofia found organic chemistry fascinating.

4. Jackie's remarks annoyed me.

5. The kitchen scene in <u>Jurassic Park</u> was frightening.

ESL 3c, Adverb Placement

1. "The Last Post" is traditionally played on Remembrance Day.

2. There never seems to be enough time.

3. My older sister is always helpful.

4. I drove fast enough to get to work on time.

5. Louis typically went to the museum with his father.

ESL 4a–c, Prepositions 1

1. I went to the movies nearly every week.

2. Francesca reads the newspaper to improve her English.

3. When we first moved to Toronto, I missed Hong Kong very much.

4. Sari shops in the grocery store everyday.

5. After his scholarship in Sardinia, Nova Scotia looked very green.

ESL 4d–f, Prepositions 2

1. Frederico was aware of the problem.

2. My brother's new glasses are for reading.

3. I walked as far as Main Street before discovering that I had left my wallet at home.

4. How much is that equal to in dollars?

5. I like to paint as well as to draw.

ESL 5a–c, Subjects and Linking Verbs

1. My school has three libraries. It will begin construction of a fourth soon.
   —or—
   My school has three libraries and will begin construction of a fourth soon.

2. Dirk's whole family is very amusing.

3. The baseball league begins its season next week.

4. This reading assignment is very long.

5. The cicadas in the trees in my neighbourhood sing all day.

ESL 5d, Expletives

1. There are three highways into downtown Montreal.

2. Here are my top choices for the position.

3. Here is the best recipe I have for turkey stuffing.

4. It is unlikely to rain when the sky is so clear.

5. There are many golf courses in Norfolk County.

ESL 6a, Questions with Who, Whom, and What

1. Who is coming to dinner?

2. What creates highway gridlock?

3. Whom did the prime minister nominate?

4. Who brings in today's mail?

5. What does the committee do?

ESL 6b, Direct versus Indirect Questions

1. How will they finance the new day-care centre?
2. Which astronomer identified and named M31?
3. Why did my family come to this country in 1848?
4. Where was the smoke coming from?
5. How does the Canadian Parliament differ from the British Parliament?

ESL 6b, Verbs and Word Order in Indirect Questions

1. He asked if I was coming or not.
2. Rupert wasn't sure when the Battle of Hastings occurred.
3. I tried to see where the rocket went.
4. The committee researched why the cost of education has outpaced inflation in the last ten years.
5. Everice asked whether I enjoy playing racquetball.

ESL 6c, Direct Quotations versus Reported Speech

1. Nino said that he loves zucchini almost as much as he loves peppers.
2. Bob told me, "I am working in the library five nights per week."
3. With a grin, Erin opined that Roger had played a faltering but passionate cello for years.
4. Mary announced, "I will be running in the Around the Bay marathon this year."
5. The company spokesperson said to wait for the third quarter results.

ESL 6d, Conditional Sentences

1. If he sees a shooting star, he makes a wish.
2. If you practise enough, you can join a band.
3. If I had practised more, I might have had my own band.
4. Wherever Fleetwood Mac performed last year, they found big audiences.
5. If the tornado had touched down, what damage would it have done?

ESL 7, Confusing Words and Phrases

1. "You look tired; maybe we should go home now?"
2. When I passed the library I remembered I needed to return a book.
3. On what basis did you decide to enroll in this class?
4. Leo's street is quiet and pleasant.
5. Annita said that this dessert was her special favourite.

SENTENCES

SENT 1a, Irrelevant Detail

1. Marx said that religion is the opium of the people.
2. Charles Dickens was a prolific author, working on up to three novels concurrently.
3. Lately the prime minister has proposed elevating several governmental posts to the rank of cabinet minister.
4. Last Thanksgiving Chuck saw the Matisse retrospective.
5. The trans-Canada highway system is now badly in need of extensive rebuilding.

SENT 1b, Illogical Constructions

1. The new bridge, still under construction, will relieve the traffic we have now.
2. They chatted like two birds until they tired.
3. The triple chocolate cake, my best dessert, was always delicious.
4. My brother wrote me a letter last week and I read it two or three times over.
5. I don't know anything about Wagner's opera <u>Parsifal</u>.

SENT 2a, Subordination

Possible rewrites:

1. Bill and Metsa, who started dating five years ago in high school, think they will get married next year.
2. Because Donovan Bailey is fast, he won a gold medal at the track and field championships.
3. I do my research at our university library because its one million plus volumes provide coverage that is both in-depth and up-to-date.
4. Stirring constantly to ensure that the butter will not brown, heat the sauce over a low flame.
5. The tulips on Parliament Hill are a gift from the Dutch people.

SENT 2c, Coordination

Possible rewrites:

1. I had a lot of reading to do every day; therefore, I did not watch television at all for months.
2. I agree with many things Robert tells me, but when I don't, I argue with him.
3. My great uncle neither smokes nor drinks.
4. He likes not only classical music but also country and western.
5. This rain is good for people; it is filling the reservoirs.

SENT 3a, Emphasis

Possible rewrites:

1. Phil told me that once the band got going and people began to dance, Hogan's party was a great success.
2. In the Maritimes, not heeding a winter storm warning can be a grave mistake.
3. I was thrilled when I first heard the plan, but now I'm not so sure.
4. Pedro is glad he took his new job, because it is challenging.
5. Because Carmen is Luis's favourite opera, he has seen it eight times.

SENT 3b, Logical Order

Possible rewrites:

1. Margaret looked happily at the Seder table: the matzos, the bitter herbs, and the single gold-rimmed cup of wine for Elijah.
2. Carter had an awful day when we were at the Skydome; he struck out in the first, fifth, and seventh innings.
3. I like a movie if it has a good story, is acted well, and ends happily.
4. In the next three hours I need to mow the lawn, shower and shave, and dress to go out.
5. As I looked around the dimly lit attic, I saw dusty boxes, piles of old clothes, and a complete human skeleton.

SENT 3c, Active Voice

Possible rewrites:

1. Paul was bitten by mosquitoes, black flies, and chiggers on his canoe trip down the Peace River.
2. Alou hit the ball deep to centre.
3. The family bought a new puppy.
4. Kurt's birthday was celebrated by everyone in our dorm.
5. Patrick called me as soon as he returned to Montreal.

SENT 4a, Sentence Variety 1

Possible rewrites:

1. Because it rained for a month, there was great flooding.
2. Quebec has a long winter, but now that I ski it seems shorter.
3. After singing every Sunday in church for years, my parents stopped last year, and now they miss it.
4. As you fly over any major Canadian city, look out the plane's window; you will be shocked by the number of swimming pools you will see.
5. Up at 5 a.m. every day, Anne never misses her gymnastics practice.

SENT 4b, Sentence Variety 2

Possible rewrites:

1. To forget all about their cares for the evening, Ali and Lynda walked in the park.
2. Walking in the park for the evening, Ali and Lynda forgot all about their cares.
3. While Ali and Lynda walked in the park for the evening, they forgot all about their cares.
4. But Ali and Lynda, walking in the park for the evening, forgot all their cares.
5. In the park, Ali and Lynda walked and forgot all their cares for the evening.

SENT 5, Misplaced and Dangling Modifiers

Possible rewrites:

1. The tools Don returned to Phil were covered with grease.
2. Fisheries and Oceans Canada wrote new rules for the Beluga Whale, which was threatened with extinction.
3. I saw him on the green walkway.
4. Young and inexperienced, Jim discovered that jobs were few and far between.
5. I wrote directions to the house for my friend.

SENT 6, Parallelism

Possible rewrites:

1. We will see Rufus on Tuesday, and Tito on Wednesday.
2. He could not swim and he would not wear a life jacket.
3. While the jet stream has remained centred on Saskatchewan, the rain has continued to fall.
4. Parliament has forgotten both the individual citizen and personal responsibility.
5. As the sun rose, the moon set.

SENT 7, Sentence Fragments

Possible rewrites:

1. My little brother is 185 cm and still growing.
2. My brother Todd swam in high school and dove in college.
3. While on vacation I read two children's books: Mireille Levert's <u>Sleep Tight</u> and Ron Lightburn's <u>Waiting for the Whales</u>.
4. Last night I saw Neville and Molly at the student union.
5. When I saw the Mona Lisa in person, I was, to be honest, disappointed.

SENT 8, Comma Splices

Possible rewrites:

1. Historians say that the Boer War marked the first time Canadian troops had been sent overseas.

2. Professor Gerson has a pleasantly acid sense of humour; accordingly, he quipped that the term <u>political ally</u> is an oxymoron.

3. I practise conga one hour every day; this has helped me improve a lot in the last year.

4. Spring in Vancouver is cool, and many visitors wish they had brought warmer clothes.

5. I am a business major, so studying economics will give me a useful background.

SENT 8, Run-ons

Possible rewrites:

1. We took a cab to the theatre. We saw <u>Show Boat</u>.

2. I hope Fred will come over and help me adjust my car's carburetor.

3. After it rained for twenty days straight, I felt like escaping to the desert.

4. I know what a typeface is, but I'm not quite sure what a font is.

5. Agriculture is still one of Canada's leading industries, and it contributes to our trade balance with the rest of the world.

WORD CHOICE

WORD 1a, Denotation

1. What are the effects of the new spending bill?
   affect: (verb) to change
   effect: (noun) a result; also (verb) to produce

2. Even if you disagree strongly with him, please be civil.
   civic: (adj) relating to a city
   civil: (adj) refraining from rudeness

3. Emile was a voracious reader.
   vociferous: (adj) loud and shouting
   voracious: (adj) eager to devour

4. Sex education has helped many teenagers get factual information on venereal diseases.
   venerable: (adj) worthy of respect
   venereal: (adj) transmitted by sexual intercourse

5. Paul, carried away by the emotional appeal of his own argument, went off on a tangent.
   tangible: (adj) something that can be touched
   tangent (go off on a tangent): (verb) to break from a line of thinking; to digress

WORD 1c, General versus Specific Words
Possible answers:

1. transportation: bus
2. foods: vegetables
3. vegetables: carrots
4. seasons: fall
5. holidays: New Year's

WORD 1c, Abstract versus Concrete Words

1. pretty: abstract
2. justice: abstract

3. leaves: concrete

4. blue: abstract

5. stars: concrete

6. wood: concrete

7. fast: abstract

8. cake: concrete

9. truth: abstract

10. shoes: concrete

WORD 1d, Idioms

1. The committee agreed to the plan.

2. Frieda left early so that she would be sure to get a good seat.

3. My niece insisted that Jell-O was superior to pudding.

4. Though we arrived early, we still had to wait in line.

5. The coach gave me some extra tips to help me try to improve my shot.

WORD 2a, Appropriateness
Possible answers:

1. Reggie disliked their new album intensely.

2. Bryan cannot come today.

3. The show was spectacular.

4. Collecting stamps was Phil's hobby.

5. If I have time, I'll eat lunch with you at noon.

WORD 3, Bias in Writing
Possible answers:

1. Our ancestors showed great courage to leave their homelands and voyage to a new and often little-known country.

2. The mayor was swamped with questions from the reporters.

3. The writing course was tailored to first-year students.

4. Who chairs that subcommittee?

5. Of all creatures on the planet, people are the most intelligent and the most destructive.

WORD 4, Wordiness

Possible answers:

1. Tom is a point guard who can play centre when necessary.
2. The test was difficult because it covered the whole semester.
3. Bad weather in Winnipeg delayed Bill's two brothers' flight, so we had to wait at the airport for them for five hours.
4. The school band, obviously unpractised, could not even play the national anthem without mistakes.
5. Why do schools of swimming fish and flocks of flying birds move with a similar coordinated motion?

WORD 5, The Dictionary

1. There are four syllables in "ob•liv•i•ous," and there are three in "ob•nox•ious."
2. marathon: a race of 26 miles, 385 yards; based upon the length of the run made by a single runner from the Greek city Marathon to Athens to tell of the Greek victory (490 B.C.) over the Persians.
3. lens: from the Latin lentil for the resemblance of a lens to the shape of the lentil bean. The double-convex lens.
4. frankfurter: a sausage originating in Frankfurt, Germany.
5. There are three syllables in "scru•pu•lous."

WORD 6, The Thesaurus

1. beautiful (adj): admirable; alluring; attractive; appealing; splendid
   (antonym): ugly
2. show (noun): drama; performance; demonstration; exposition; fair
   (verb): bare; reveal; exhibit; expose; divulge
   (antonym): (verb) hide
3. prise (verb): lever open; pry open; force; wrench; obtain with difficulty
   (antonym): close
4. document (noun): certificate; charter; deed; form; instrument
   (verb): chronicle; list; log; note; write down
   (antonym): (verb) destroy records

5. industrious (adj): busy; conscientious; assiduous; diligent; earnest
   (antonym): lazy

WORD 7, Usage

1. I thought we could leave, but Joe is not ready to go.
2. Nicholas loved music of all types, but Lou was very particular.
3. Although I set out 20 tomato plants this summer, none has any ripe fruit yet.
4. The show that is on Channel 42 at 10 tonight should be very interesting.
5. Jason should have arrived by now.

EDITING FOR GRAMMAR

EDIT 1a–d, Subject–Verb Agreement 1

1. The ticket, including dinner with dessert, a floor show, and dancing after, is only twenty dollars.

2. The smell of the ripening apples and pears attracts bees to the orchard.

3. Neither my parents nor my brother wants to try my latest culinary triumph—cranberry-tofu meat loaf.

4. The House's minority make their voices heard.

5. High tides and wind create dangerous conditions along the coast.

EDIT 1e–l, Subject–Verb Agreement 2

1. Anyone who studies regularly will do better in school and enjoy it more.

2. All the explanations are inadequate.

3. None of my classes meets before 10 A.M.

4. There are, on a regulation baseball team, nine players.

5. Politics both fascinates and repulses him.

EDIT 2a–b, Principal Parts of Irregular Verbs

1. If you bend the pipe more, I think it will fit.

2. After John sat down, he pulled out a book and dozed off.

3. Having taken the subway for years, I was not easily surprised by unusual-looking passengers.

4. Paul took the dinner roast out at noon because it was frozen.

5. Having dug the trench, the workers laid the new gas line.

EDIT 2c, Verb Tense

1. PRESENT PERFECT: I have gone to the All-Star Game every year.

2. PRESENT PROGRESSIVE: I am going to the All-Star Game this year.

3. PRESENT PERFECT PROGRESSIVE: I have been going to the All-Star Game every year.

4. PAST: I went to the All-Star Game every year until last year.

5. PAST PERFECT: I had gone to the All-Star Game every year until last year.

EDIT 2e, Verb Mood

1. (subjunctive) Bob asked <u>that he come early today.</u>
   IMPERATIVE: Come early today.

2. (subjunctive) <u>If I were training harder,</u> I would be better prepared.
   INDICATIVE: Because I was training harder, I was better prepared.

3. (indicative) <u>Every night he reads until bedtime.</u>
   SUBJUNCTIVE: I asked that he read every night until bedtime.

4. (imperative) Cheryl said, "<u>Hurry up,</u> or we'll miss the bus."
   INDICATIVE: Cheryl told us to hurry up or we'd miss the bus.

5. (subjunctive) <u>I wished it were snowing,</u> but it was only raining.
   INDICATIVE: I wished for snow, but got only rain.

EDIT 2f, Active and Passive Voices

1. (passive) The letters were mailed by Jamal after lunch.

2. (active) Dominique cooked the dinner.

3. (passive) <u>La Petite Noirceur</u> was written by Jean Larose.

4. (passive) The Blue Line bus was seen by Regina.

5. (active) Many people who rarely watch baseball otherwise, watch the World Series.

EDIT 3a–c, Shifts 1

1. The United Nations' membership has grown steadily, and it adds one or more new members nearly every year. (number shift)

2. When I study, I usually work for at least three hours. (tense shift)

3. Once people swim in this lake, especially in August, they never want to swim anywhere else. (person shift)

4. My father worked for 42 years; he retired last month. (tense shift)

5. Let's take the 10:37 train to Batoche. (person and mood shifts)

EDIT 3d–g, Shifts 2

1. I went to the new restaurant on Elm Street and enjoyed the meal. (subject shift)

2. Newsprint recycling requires extensive sophisticated processing, such as the de-inking of paper and the handling of the heavy metals extracted. (style shift)

3. Arlene said, "I read an interesting story in <u>La Presse</u> and you should read it too." (quotation shift)

4. We sat on the broken down bus until the Transit Commission sent a replacement. (subject shift; dangling modifier)

5. The school's main entrance was an imposing series of granite steps and landings leading up to a pair of great carved oak doors. Inside, the hallways were dark and long. (perspective shift: outside view to inside view)

EDIT 4, Pronoun Agreement

1. The faculty votes for its officers every October.

2. He needs to better train his dog Biff, who barks at the letter carrier every day.

3. Neither Mrs. Williams nor Mr. Williams remembered her or his birthday.

4. When Louisa and Hal come to visit, they always bring their dog.

5. Each player in the tournament took a turn at the table.

EDIT 5, Pronoun Reference

1. Last night on the Fifth Concession, Adriano saw eight deer, which was unusual.

2. Professor Marilee Tecknor, who studies retroviruses and has isolated a new subclass, gave a lecture on retroviruses at our seminar.

3. Although I know that supply-side economics focuses on production, and demand-side economics emphasizes consumption, this knowledge has never helped me understand where my paycheque goes every week.

4. When the company demanded a cut in wages and benefits, the union leadership recommended a strike vote be taken.

5. When tours come through our town, they often stop at the Shelburne Museum to see its extensive American folk art collection.

EDIT 6a–e, Pronoun Case 1

1. Have you seen my brother?

2. After taking the subway, Chuck and I went to the deli.

3. If it were up to Laura and me, we'd leave now.

4. The boss appreciated their working on Saturday night.

5. My sister said she would be going to visit our grandmother after visiting Susan and me.

EDIT 6f–i, Pronoun Case 2

1. Professor Mbutuze asked Dave and me to participate in the experiment.

2. Despite all his campaigning, the Ottawa Citizen reported that the incumbent was running stronger than he.

3. My sister, who has incredible hearing when it comes to the telephone, yelled out from the shower, "Whom is that call for?"

4. With two runners on, Cheryl and me, our best hitter came to the plate.

5. The victory will go to whoever crosses the finish line first.

EDIT 7, Adjectives and Adverbs

1. Laura grew more and more happy as the semester progressed.

2. I think it's colder today than yesterday.

3. The Canada Council is charged with administering these kinds of literary awards.

4. He is doing well in pottery class.

5. With two of their starters on the disabled list, things look bad for the Montreal Expos.

PUNCTUATION

PUNCT 1a, The Period

1. If you know the Latin meaning abbreviated by a.m. and p.m., you will find it easier to remember which one to use.
2. One of the experimental drugs being used to combat AIDS is AZT.
3. I wondered if he knew what the initials OPP stood for.
4. One of the most resounding scenes in all of Shakespeare is in <u>King Lear</u> V.iii.
5. Tintin's best friend is Capt. Horatio Haddock.

PUNCT 1b–c, The Question Mark and Exclamation Point

1. Louis asked me which class I liked best.
2. Joyce said, "Do you know whether bus or subway is the better way to get to St. Clair Avenue from here?"
3. As usual for this region, the weather was sunny.
4. Which route to Antigonish has less traffic, John wanted to know.
5. "Can I come too?" my sister asked.

PUNCT 2a–c, The Comma 1

1. He worked hard, yet he was not feeling tired.
2. As Felix watched, the cat ate her breakfast of Tuna Delight.
3. Last semester I had Professor Roop for history, which has always been my favourite subject.
4. Yawning, Susan put down her book and went to bed.
5. My oldest brother, Geoffrey, usually comes for Thanksgiving.

PUNCT 2d–g, The Comma 2

1. The recipe specifically called for large ripe red tomatoes.
2. This fall Eliot was reading Chaucer, Shakespeare, and Milton.
3. For this reason, the committee voted to change the policy.

4. The trade surplus has declined this year, unlike previous years.

5. Riding into a head wind can help you improve your cycling endurance, power, and technique.

PUNCT 2h–l, The Comma 3

1. I smiled and said, "Yes, I'll be there."

2. If you want to call, Phil has a phone.

3. Our reservations are for Friday, August 19, through Sunday, August 28.

4. Luke called yesterday and said, "Congratulations on your new baby."

5. Lonnie gave me a ride from Calgary, Alberta, to Winnipeg, Manitoba.

PUNCT 2m, The Comma 4

1. John and his brother watched <u>Road to Avonlea</u> every week.

2. I drove last week to Fredericton, New Brunswick, to visit my best friends.

3. The critics panned the play <u>The Quiet Canadian</u> as slow and pretentious.

4. If I were you, I would leave before rush hour.

5. The small gold locket was a family heirloom.

PUNCT 3, The Semicolon

1. The drive from Whitehorse to Dawson was long, but I didn't mind, nor did my sister.

2. The rapid decrease in computer hardware prices has put pressure on software developers to do the same; nonetheless, they have resisted the trend for the most part.

3. Last year I saw <u>Jurassic Park</u>, which used extensive computer animation; <u>In the Line of Fire</u>, which showed electronically manipulated "historical" photographs; and <u>Until the End of the World</u>, which presented computer-driven dream exploration—technology is now both a major theme and tool of the film studios.

4. I was shocked when I drove the new $20 000 car; it rode only a bit better than my current car, which has a book value of only $1500.

5. Although I support universal access to health care, I disagree with waste; providing access shouldn't eliminate the option of user fees.

PUNCT 4, The Colon

1. I have passed along to my children one of my father's sayings: "When you borrow something, try to return it in better condition than you received it."

2. Scientists, in an effort to isolate what it is in food that makes most people evaluate it as "tasting good or delicious," have determined the single most important ingredient: fat.

3. On your way home could you pick up a kilogram of cold cuts, a head of lettuce, and a video.

4. Today is a very good day for haying: plenty of sunshine, a light breeze, and low humidity.

5. We took the following route: Highway 80 to Rock Springs, Highway 187 to Farson, and Highway 28 to South Pass City.

PUNCT 5, The Apostrophe

1. We spent the day at Canada's Wonderland.

2. My grandmother told me that the '38 hurricane was much worse than this year's storm.

3. A snake sheds its skin when it's growing.

4. What is our company's policy regarding maternity leave?

5. I thought it was hers, but perhaps it's really Bill's.

PUNCT 6, Quotation Marks

1. "Where you place your commas is one of my teacher's 'things,' so I always doublecheck my work," said Elaine.

2. "Would you like to come to dinner with us?" Mary asked.

3. When I read computer magazines I find all the technobabble confusing: RAM, ROM, and bytes—who dreams up these terms?

4. Milan told me that he had written his term paper in just two hours.

5.   "I hope you'll come to our party tonight," said Alison.

   "Me too," I replied, "but I have to work until 11."

   "That's no problem," she said. "It doesn't even start until 10, and I doubt you'll miss anything. Just come as you are after work."

PUNCT 7, Other Punctuation

1. One awkward, but acceptable, solution to the problem of sexism in pronouns is the use of <u>him/her </u>as well as <u>he or she</u>.

2. When in Rome—as the saying goes—do as the Romans.

3. The snowmobile—known to many as the Skidoo—was invented in Canada by Armand Bombardier.

4. "Our class meets in that new science building. What's its name? Something Hall ... Burstein ... Gurstein? I can't remember," said John.

5. I still remember the opening lines to Shakespeare's Sonnet LXXIII: "That time of year thou mayst in me behold / When yellow leaves, or none, or few, do hang / Upon those boughs which shake against the cold."

MECHANICS

MECH 1a–d, Capitals 1

1. Unfortunately, stargazers living this far north can't see the Southern Cross.

2. When Tom "Tiny" Anderson sang last week at the 3rd Avenue Grill, the crowd roared its approval.

3. The cold war may be over, but we're still paying the bill.

4. The Baptist church in my town sponsors a community food shelf.

5. In the last four months the Fraser and Ottawa rivers reached record flood levels, but the Liard River was below normal.

MECH 1e–k, Capitals 2

1. In a recent article, economist Roy Brown wrote, "For the first time in our history, by the year 2000, fifty percent of all Canadian jobs will require at least one year of college."

2. I read the Welland Tribune every day to keep up on local news.

3. During the spring semester I am going to enroll in calculus, history, and English.

4. I think she bought one of the new Apple notebook computers.

5. Who reports on the news media? The news media does.

MECH 2, Abbreviations

1. He reported to Sergeant Preston.

2. The prime minister announced that the new policy was designed to protect our national energy program.

3. Aristotle was born in 384 B.C.

4. Dr. James Wrinton gave the keynote address. —or—
   James Wrinton, M.D. gave the keynote address. [MD and M.D. are both acceptable]

5. For the trip they packed clothes, food, games, and so forth.

MECH 3, Numbers

1. Armand cut the plank into 4 two-metre sections.

2. Marc Garneau became the first Canadian in space aboard the shuttle <u>Challenger</u> on Oct. 5, 1984.

3. Skosh thought the cost of the ferry ride was more than $20. [or twenty dollars]

4. British Columbia has more than 1900 elementary and secondary schools.

5. Over the holidays we saw four films, two plays, and thirteen videos. [or 4 films, 2 plays, and 13 videos]

MECH 4, Italics/Underlining

1. Linda likes Microsoft <u>Word</u>, but I prefer Claris <u>MacWrite</u>.

2. The most commonly occurring word in English is <u>the</u>.

3. I asked him to explain what <u>noblesse oblige</u> means.

4. Did you read last week's cover story in <u>Saturday Night</u>?

5. Tina asked if he would like a glass of chablis.

MECH 5, The Hyphen

1. I am very close to my brother-in-law.

2. The ex-Varsity halfback joined our club and boosted our whole team.

3. Are you looking forward to the beginning of the school year?

4. Our class voted twenty-one to seventeen for more study time.

5. In pre-Confederation Canada many people lived on farms.

MECH 6a, Words that Sound Alike

1. In our library, serial acquisitions is on the 3rd floor.

2. In the 100-metre finals, Sarah was third and I was fourth.

3. My father is site manager for the new Deeter Building construction project.

4. My teacher recommended that we always read the foreword, as it usually defines the scope and approach of the book that follows.

5. All the people I know with personal stationery are of my parents' generation.

MECH 6b, Basic Spelling Rules

1. I'm hoping we can see Jeri before she leaves.

2. Professor Guimard is very knowledgeable about plate tectonics.

3. Lofti Zadeh was lying down thinking when an idea suddenly occurred to him; half an hour later he had laid out all the fundamentals of the field now known as Fuzzy Logic.

4. How much did you say you paid for those peaches?

5. I sent the package via Express, so he ought to receive it by noon tomorrow.

MECH 6c, Commonly Misspelled Words

1. John's horse, like most quarter horses, has a good temperament.

2. Parents frequently sacrifice for their children.

3. Our school has an excellent guidance counsellor.

4. What is your interpretation of these statistics?

5. I would like to go, whether Donna comes or not.

ESSENTIALS OF FORMATTING

FORMAT 1a–b, Basic Computer Formatting

    (a)   <u>top of page</u> to <u>last name/page number</u>: 1.25 cm (1/2 inch)

1. (b)   top margin: 2.5 cm (1 inch)
2. (c)   left margin: 2.5 cm (1 inch)
3. (d)   bottom margin: 2.5 cm (1 inch)
4. (e)   right margin: 2.5 cm (1 inch)
5. (f)   linespacing: double-spaced

FORMAT 2, Formatting Papers Using MLA Guidelines

    (a)   <u>top of page</u> to <u>last name/page number</u>: 1.25 cm (1/2 inch)

1. (b)   top and bottom margins: 2.5 cm (1 inch)
2. (c)   linespacing: double-spaced
3. (d)   left margin: 2.5 cm (1 inch)
4. (e)   right margin: 2.5 cm (1 inch)
5. "Smith page 3" should instead be "Smith 3"-- "page" shouldn't be written out.

FORMAT 2, Formatting Papers Using APA Guidelines

    (a)   <u>top of page</u> to <u>last name/page number</u>: 1.25 cm (1/2 inch)

1. (b)   top and bottom margins: 2.5 cm (1 inch)
2. (c)   linespacing: double-spaced
3. (d)   left margin: 2.5 cm (1 inch)
4. (e)   right margin: 2.5 cm (1 inch)
5. "Smith page 3" should instead be "Rise and Fall 3"-- the student's name is not included, nor is the word "page," and the page number should be preceded by a shortened version of the paper's title (here given as "Rise and Fall").

FORMAT 3, Formatting a Business Letter

(a) <u>top of page</u> to <u>top of return address</u>: 6-12 linespaces (use this variation to balance the letter visually on the page from top to bottom)

1. (b) linespacing: single-spaced throughout.
Check spaces between blocks as they should not all be the same; that is, add space between the date and internal address; internal address and salutation; between the salutation and body text; between text blocks; between the last text block and the close; between the close and signature; and between the signature and notations (if any).

2. (c) left margin; 2.5 cm (1 inch)

3. (d) bottom margin: in a single-page business letter, such as this one, there is no standard bottom margin; instead the bottom margin floats in accord with how you set the top margin.

4. (e) right margin; 2.5 cm (1 inch)

5. Appropriate letter type: (full block; modified block; indented)? Full block; it is the most formal and therefore most appropriate for this purpose.

THE LIBRARY

LIB 1-4, Library Resources, a crossword puzzle:

Down

2. Used to locate books within the stacks. **CALLNUMBER**

3. Acroynm for Compact Disc, Read-Only Memory. **CDROM**

4. Good source of geographical information, especially maps. **ATLAS**

5. Abbreviation most often used when referring to the World Wide Web. **WWW**

6. Most authorative historical dictionary of the English language. **OXFORDENGLISH**

Across

1. Generally an excellent first resource for a topic new to you. **ENCYCLOPEDIA**

5. Source of brief biographical sketches on contemporary Americans. **WHOSWHOINAMERICA**

10. Author of a very useful guide to the guides. **SHEEHY**

12. Best known guide to popular periodical literature. **READERSGUIDE**

13. Term meaning any store of information, typically large and accessed by computer. **DATABASE**

THE RESEARCH PAPER

RESCH 4b, Integrating Quotations—see your instructor.

There are infinitely many possible "correct" ways to incorporate these quotations. Therefore, you will need to work with your instructor to review your work for this exercise.

RESCH 4d, Avoiding Plagiarism—see your instructor.

There are infinitely many possible "correct" ways to incorporate these quotations. Therefore, you will need to work with your instructor to review your work for this exercise.

MLA STYLE DOCUMENTATION

MLA DOCU 1, MLA In-Text Citations

Note: Possible answers are provided but many other valid solutions exist.

1. The fantasy genre has always supported the concept of a separate, sometimes superior, animal wisdom: "Human beings say, 'It never rains but it pours.' This is not very apt, for it frequently does rain without pouring. The rabbits' proverb is better expressed. They say, 'One cloud feels lonely'" (Adams, 184; ch. 23).

2. The fantasy genre has always supported the concept of a separate, sometimes superior, animal wisdom. In <u>Watership Down</u>, Richard Adams's narrator gently chides the reader: "Human beings say, 'It never rains but it pours.' This is not very apt, for it frequently does rain without pouring. The rabbits' proverb is better expressed. They say, 'One cloud feels lonely'" (184; ch. 23).

3. Though they exist in infinite variety, clouds have a simple shared origin: "A cloud is a collection of water droplets or ice crystals in the air. It is formed when water vapor is cooled and changed into water droplets or ice crystals" (Heimler and Neal 234).

4. Heimler and Neal point out in <u>Principles</u> that though clouds exist in infinite variety, they have a simple shared origin: "A cloud is a collection of water droplets or ice crystals in the air. It is formed when water vapor is cooled and changed into water droplets or ice crystals" (234).

5. As Symington observed, "NATO's muddled expansion is so fraught with competing strategies that it has simultaneously threatened Moscow and made overtures to Russia to join the alliance itself" ("Crossroads" 267).

OTHER SYSTEMS OF DOCUMENTATION

OTHER DOCU 2, APA-Style References

References

American Jazz Museum.(1975). <u>All that jazz!:</u> <u>America's truest voice</u>. Phoenix, AZ: Fine Press.

Baxandall, R., Gordono, L., & Rooli, S. (Eds.). (1983). <u>Hard singing, hard living: American women who sang the blues</u>. New York: Phantom Press.

Garraty, J. B. (Ed.). (1982). <u>The musical '50's</u>. Chicago: University of Chicago Press.

Guenter, L. (1990). <u>Up all night: A history of the blues</u>. New York: Melody Press.

Gutman, S. N.(1977). <u>The music business</u>. New York: Phantom Press.

American Jazz Museum. (1975). All that
    jazz!: America's truest voice. Phoenix,
    AZ: Fine Press.

MN437
.A99
1975

Baxandall, R., Gordono, L., Rooli,S. (Eds.).
    (1983). Hard singing, hard living:
    American women who sang the blues.
    New York: Phantom Press, 1983.

MM438
.B376
1983

Garraty, J. B. (Ed.). (1982). The musical
    '50's. Chicago: University of Chicago
    Press.

MN248
.G12
1982

Guenter, Larry. (1990). Up all night: A
    history of the blues. New York:
    Melody Press.

MN437
.G554
1990

Gutman, Stanley N. (1977). The music
    business. New York: Phantom Press.

MN439
.G229
1977